Chemistry

CONCEPTS AND APPLICATIONS

CHEMISTRY AND INDUSTRY

GLENCOE

McGraw-Hill

New York, New York   Columbus, Ohio   Woodland Hills, California   Peoria, Illinois

Chemistry
Concepts and Applications

Student Edition

Teacher Wraparound Edition

Teacher Classroom Resources:

Laboratory Manual SE and TE

Study Guide SE and TE

Problems and Solutions Manual

Supplemental Practice Problems SE and TE

Chapter Review and Assessment

Section Focus Transparency Package

Basic Concepts Transparency Package

Problem Solving Transparency Package

ChemLab and MiniLab Worksheets

Critical Thinking/Problem Solving

Chemistry and Industry

Consumer Chemistry

Tech Prep Applications

Applying Scientific Methods in Chemistry

Spanish Resources

Lesson Plans

Calculator-based Labs

Technology

Computer Test Bank: Windows and Macintosh

CD-ROM Multimedia System: Windows and
Macintosh Versions

Videodisc Program

Chapter Summaries, English and Spanish
Audiocassettes

MindJogger Videoquizzes

Mastering Concepts in Chemistry - Software

The Glencoe Science Professional Development Series

Cooperative Learning in the Science Classroom

Alternate Assessment in the Science Classroom

Lab and Safety Skills in the Science Classroom

Performance Assessment in the Science Classroom

Using the Internet in the Science Classroom

Glencoe/McGraw-Hill

A Division of The McGraw-Hill Companies

Send all inquiries to:
Glencoe/McGraw-Hill
8787 Orion Place
Columbus, Ohio 43240-4027

ISBN 0-02-827488-1
Printed in the United States of America.

4 5 6 7 8 9   024   03 02 01 00

Contents

To the Teacher

This ***Chemistry and Industry*** book provides 15 articles on important industrial processes to supplement ***Chemistry: Concepts and Applications.*** These articles show students how the concepts and phenomena they have learned in chemistry are applied in the "real" world. Most of the articles deal with the production of recognizable materials students use every day, such as paper, glass, soaps, and flavorings. Other articles explore the use of compounds with which students may not be as familiar but are nontheless important in their everyday lives; compounds such as sulfuric acid, benzene, and ammonia.

These articles are appropriate enrichments for all students. Questions at the end of each article highlight the important points and help students better understand the applications of chemistry.

Paper: Just What Really Goes into Each Piece?

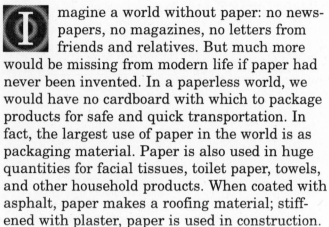 magine a world without paper: no newspapers, no magazines, no letters from friends and relatives. But much more would be missing from modern life if paper had never been invented. In a paperless world, we would have no cardboard with which to package products for safe and quick transportation. In fact, the largest use of paper in the world is as packaging material. Paper is also used in huge quantities for facial tissues, toilet paper, towels, and other household products. When coated with asphalt, paper makes a roofing material; stiffened with plaster, paper is used in construction.

Paper comes in many grades and weights. The heaviest and thickest is used to make plasterboard. Cardboard is excellent for packing everything from refrigerators and air conditioners to lightweight cameras and stereo components. Artists use special fine paper for sketching and drawing. Many people use beautifully made writing paper for their letters and documents. Coarser paper fills school notebooks and memo books. Coated paper is used in magazines, where accurate reproduction of color is important. The cheapest paper is used for newspapers, paper napkins, and facial tissues. Paper has even replaced coarse textiles in many products such as rug backings and certain types of bags. Modern life would be hard to imagine without paper.

Paper was invented in China. Archaeological evidence suggests that it was already in use by the beginning of the first century A.D. The first historical record mentioning paper comes from A.D. 105, when a Chinese court official named Ts'ai Lun presented his own brand of paper to the emperor. The oldest piece of paper we have dates from A.D. 264.

Paper can be made by dipping a fine-mesh screen into a vat of cellulose fibers suspended in water. This mixture is called the pulp. Some of the water drains through the mesh; the rest evaporates when the paper is hung up to dry. Dry paper does not crumble because the cellulose strands are hooked together by tiny hairlike fibers called fibrils.

It took nearly a thousand years for the Chinese technique of paper-making to reach Europe. Demand for the product was low in the West until the Renaissance brought with it both increased literacy and a desire for information. The invention of the printing press in the middle of the fifteenth century also heightened the need for paper. Paper was scarce at this time because it was made from rag fibers—often literally from old clothes—and demand exceeded supply. Moreover, paper was made by hand; a good worker could produce no more than 750 sheets a day.

All this changed during the Industrial Revolution of the eighteenth century. First of all, the steps in paper-making became mechanized. By 1804, English paper-makers were using a highly efficient device based on the ideas of two French brothers, Henry and Sealy Fourdrinier. The first Fourdrinier machine in America began operation in 1827. Another way of mechanizing paper-making, by using a cylinder-type machine, was developed in the United States in 1817. Over the years, though, the Fourdrinier device proved more popular.

As these mechanical developments were going on, various processes were discovered that allowed pulp to be made from wood and other readily available plant substances. The object of the pulping process is to separate the plant into its individual cellulose fibers. The process most commonly used today, known as kraft pulping, (*kraft* comes from the German word meaning strong) was developed by German chemist Carl F. Dahl in 1884.

In the kraft process, wood chips are heated under pressure with a solution of sodium hydroxide, sodium sulfide, and sodium sulfate. The resulting pulp is filtered and then beaten, usually in a machine called a Hollander beater. This process of squeezing and pounding causes the wood's cellulose fibers to swell and become flexible. It also separates the cellulose fibrils that add strength to the paper.

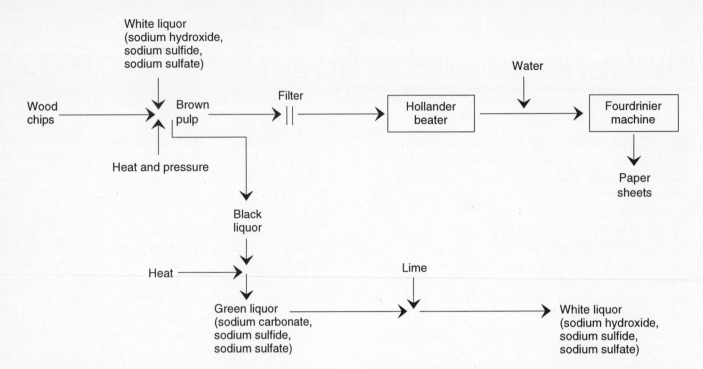

The pulp, which is dark brown in color, is used for packaging as paper bags, wrapping paper, and boxes. If the pulp is to be made into writing or printing paper, it must be bleached first.

To form sheets of paper, the pulp is mixed with a large amount of water. (The usual ratio is 99 percent water to 1 percent pulp.) The pulp spreads evenly over a continuously moving wire screen, which then enters the Fourdrinier machine. There the pulp is pressed by rollers, dried, and finally wound onto a huge roll for shipment.

The kraft process is highly self-sufficient, making it both economically and environmentally sound. When the brown pulp is produced, it is washed with water and filtered. The resulting *black liquor,* which contains organic matter and other substances, is first concentrated, then burned in a power boiler. The combustion of the organic matter produces heat, which is used to power a turbine by means of high-pressure steam. The turbine produces electricity that is used in the factory to continue the manufacturing process. The remaining inorganic substances from the black liquor—sodium carbonate, sodium sulfide, and sodium sulfate—are dissolved in water to produce a *green liquor*. This solution is filtered and treated with lime, which converts the sodium carbonate into sodium hydroxide, creating a *white liquor* that contains the original pulping chemicals.

The main reason paper is so cheap, and thus universal, lies in the efficiency of this chemical recovery system. A little sodium sulfate is lost, but even this can be recovered from the bleaching chemicals or from so-called tall oil, which is formed from the wood's resin and fatty acids as a by-product of the process. Methanol, another by-product of kraft pulping, can be recovered and burned as fuel. A properly run kraft pulp mill will be nearly self-sustaining in energy.

Because of its efficiency and cheapness, the kraft process accounts for some two-thirds of the paper produced in the world today. Other methods are still used, however. In the sulfite pulping process, wood chips are cooked under high pressure in a solution of sulfur dioxide and a hydrogen sulfite of either calcium, magnesium, sodium, or ammonium. This process is not quite as economical as the kraft process, but the resulting paper is very fine and can easily be bleached to a high degree of whiteness. This method is used to produce fine writing paper.

Taken together, the kraft and sulfite processes generate over 80 percent of the wood pulp produced in the United States.

A process called mechanical pulping is very efficient in that the yield of pulp from each piece of wood is much higher than in other processes. The cellulose fibers are torn apart mechanically as the wood is pressed against a wet grindstone or is passed between revolving metal disks called refiners. However, the fibers are badly damaged by the grinding, and the result is a weaker paper than that produced by the kraft or sulfite processes. Mechanical pulping produces about 10 percent of America's paper. Many newspapers are printed on paper made from mechanical pulp.

Because the kraft process is so self-contained, its effect on the environment is relatively benign. The substances in the black liquor would cause terrible pollution if they were released into outside fresh water, but they are all reused to continue the process. Other by-products also are kept from the environment because they are commercially valuable. Turpentine, extracted from the wood during pulping, is important as a paint remover. Tall oil, when not reused, is refined to produce rosin and fatty acids, two useful chemicals. Methanol, a condensate from black liquor, is either burned as fuel or sold.

Modern paper mills also use extremely efficient filters on their smokestacks, along with other particle-control devices, resulting in a 99 percent control efficiency. Odorous compounds have been reduced 80 percent since 1974, even as production rose by 30 percent. The industry also lowered sulfur dioxide emissions through energy conservation, boiler upgrading, and fuel switching (use of wood residue with low sulfur dioxide content).

The most important ingredient in the paper-making process, of course, is wood, and many conservationists are concerned that America's demand for paper will destroy its forests. In general, the nation's wood supply is stable because many companies that use wood replant trees, sometimes on their own tree farms. Scientific forest management techniques have reduced soil erosion and resulted in faster-growing trees that are stronger and more insect-resistant.

A growing interest in preserving America's forests for as long as possible has led to an increase in recycling. Recycling of paper, appropriately enough, began in China only a few centuries after Ts'ai Lun's gift to the emperor, and this technology also diffused westward. In 1800, an Englishman named Mathias Koops was granted a patent for a method of recycling. By the 1950s, many paper companies were using waste paper as their primary manufacturing source. Commitment to recycling increased dramatically starting in the 1970s, as people became more aware of threats to the environment. By the mid-1980s, about 30 percent of all paper made in the United States came from reclaimed fiber.

There are two methods of paper recovery used in reclaiming of fiber. If the finished paper will be used for printing (about 6 percent of the total) a de-inking process is used. Waste paper, including used corrugated boxes, old newspapers, and office waste, is fed into a large tank called a pulper, where it is mixed with hot water, caustic soda, and other substances. Metal blades agitate the mix and separate the fibers. The pulp is filtered to remove unwanted particles, and washed to eliminate any residual ink. Sometimes, it is bleached with hypochlorite. If de-inking is not necessary, a second process is used, in which most of the substances are eliminated. This kind of recycled paper is used mostly for cartons and packaging materials.

The making of paper thus has an interesting and complex history. If the challenges involved in reusing resources and protecting the environment can be met, paper will continue to be available in abundance, meeting our needs as it has in the past.

1. What were the two factors that limited the amount of paper in use before the Industrial Revolution?

_____

_____

2. In a finished piece of paper, what holds the cellulose fibers together and gives the paper its strength?

_____

_____

3. Three substances used in the kraft pulping process are NaOH, Na$_2$S, and Na$_2$SO$_4$. Write the names of these substances.

_____

_____

_____

4. Describe the use and recovery of sodium hydroxide in the kraft pulping process.

_____

_____

_____

5. List one advantage and one disadvantage of the mechanical pulping process.

_____

_____

_____

6. Compared to the first method developed in ancient China, how does the modern paper-making process reduce labor costs?

_____

_____

_____

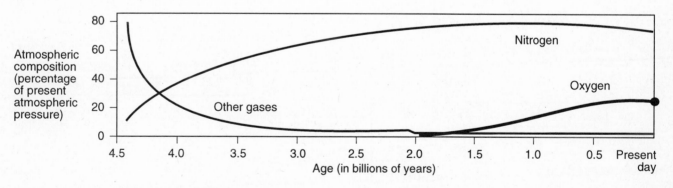

Oxygen: More Than Thin Air

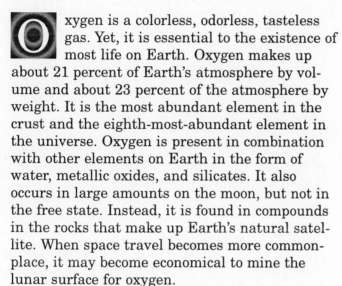

xygen is a colorless, odorless, tasteless gas. Yet, it is essential to the existence of most life on Earth. Oxygen makes up about 21 percent of Earth's atmosphere by volume and about 23 percent of the atmosphere by weight. It is the most abundant element in the crust and the eighth-most-abundant element in the universe. Oxygen is present in combination with other elements on Earth in the form of water, metallic oxides, and silicates. It also occurs in large amounts on the moon, but not in the free state. Instead, it is found in compounds in the rocks that make up Earth's natural satellite. When space travel becomes more commonplace, it may become economical to mine the lunar surface for oxygen.

Oxygen is a highly reactive element and forms strong bonds with itself and with atoms of most other elements. Thus, oxygen does not occur on Earth in the form of individual atoms. In air, oxygen exists as molecules, each made up of two oxygen atoms bonded together. Oxygen

supports combustion. In combustion reactions, substances combine with the oxygen to form new compounds, giving off energy. Chemical reactions with oxygen can be as rapid and violent as an explosion or as slow and quiet as the rusting of iron.

Although oxygen is now abundant in the atmosphere, it is a relative latecomer there. The early atmosphere probably contained a small amount of oxygen released from water that was irradiated with ultraviolet (UV) rays from the sun. However, a large concentration of oxygen was not available until life evolved. Some cells developed the ability to acquire hydrogen from water, releasing the oxygen in the process. The oxygen was a chemical pollutant in the atmosphere, probably poisoning many early forms of life that were not adapted to it. Much of the newly released oxygen combined with iron in the oceans and rocks, producing huge deposits of red iron ore that clearly mark the time period when the change occurred.

Atmospheric composition (percentage of present atmospheric pressure)

Age (in billions of years)

One form of oxygen, called ozone (O_3), plays an important role in the environmental health of the planet. Ozone is present as a layer in the upper atmosphere. The ozone layer is a thin band located between 25 and 35 km above the surface of Earth. In the upper atmosphere, oxygen molecules absorb UV radiation from the sun and break apart into two oxygen atoms. The single oxygen atoms then form bonds with diatomic

oxygen molecules, forming ozone molecules. These new molecules absorb more UV radiation at slightly different wavelengths than the oxygen. The absorption of damaging solar radiation by ozone helps to protect the living organisms on the planet surface below. The absorption of UV by this gaseous substance is so efficient that at wavelengths near 250 nm in the UV range, only 1 part in 10^{30} of the incoming solar radiation penetrates the ozone layer. Much research is being conducted to determine the effects of chemical pollutants on the ozone layer because its destruction could lead to increases in health problems, including cataracts and skin cancer.

Ozone also forms when an electrical discharge passes through oxygen gas. Consequently, this pungent, irritating blue gas can be detected near electrical equipment and after lightning storms. The odor many people associate with "clean air" after a thunderstorm is, in reality, that of ozone. Because ozone would be encountered in airplane cabins on commercial flights at altitudes above 15 km, the incoming air is passed through filters that decompose the ozone to ordinary oxygen. Near Earth's surface, ozone is a pollutant. Atmospheric ozone attacks the carbon-carbon double bonds in rubber and contributes to its weathering. Hence, many rubber-containing products such as automobile tires and bicycle tires crack and deteriorate as a result of exposure to ozone.

One method of producing pure oxygen is to pass an electrical current through water. However, this process uses great amounts of energy and, as such, is very expensive. Because air is 21 percent oxygen, processes involving the retrieval of this gas from air are most economical. Oxygen is separated from the nitrogen, carbon dioxide, and trace gases found in air by use of a process called fractional distillation. The process relies on the fact that at a given pressure, different substances have different boiling points. Ordinary air is liquefied using high pressures and low temperatures. When heat is applied to the liquid air in a distillation column, each component vaporizes at a different temperature and can be drawn off separately and turned back to a liquid. The production of oxygen is most cost effective for very large oxygen plants that can produce 2000 metric tons or more a day. In Europe, an oxygen pipeline 956 km long serves France, Germany, Belgium, and the Netherlands.

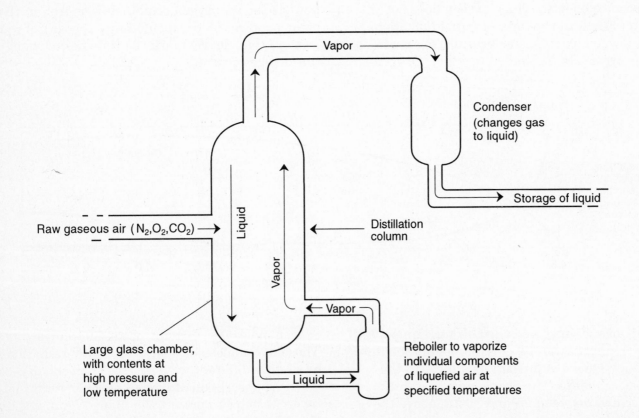

Basic Fractional Distillation Process

Oxygen is used in industry in chemical reactions for producing other chemicals, for welding, and for oxyacetylene and oxyhydrogen torches that can reach temperatures of almost 3500°C. The use of pure oxygen in welding improves efficiency and makes cutting torches useful even underwater. Pure oxygen has come to replace the old open-hearth furnaces that were once used in refining raw steel. Oxygen is introduced into molten iron and scrap, where it combines with carbon and other undesirable elements there, so the impurities can be removed. This new process is much faster than the hearth method. Liquid oxygen, a pale-blue liquid that forms at −185°C, is used to support combustion in liquid-fuel rockets. Small amounts of oxygen are produced for medical applications in hospitals and home-care situations. Some oxygen is also carried on board airplanes for emergencies at high altitudes, because the concentration of atmospheric oxygen available decreases as altitude increases.

Many industrial processes produce large volumes of hot water. The hot water was once returned to the rivers or lakes from which the water was originally taken. That caused heating of the rivers and lakes. However, as temperature increases, the amount of oxygen in water decreases. The loss of oxygen in lakes, rivers, ponds, and streams was of concern because gaseous oxygen must be available to support fishes and other organisms living in the water. In addition to the support of plant and animal life, enough additional oxygen must be available in the water to support the biological breakdown of the organisms after they die. The misuse of lakes and streams in many instances had almost fully depleted the dissolved oxygen available for life support and has given rise to "dead" lakes and streams. This condition is called thermal pollution. Today, industrial plants must restore the water they use to a temperature very near the natural temperature of the original water system in order to preserve the oxygen content of the water system.

1. In what sense was oxygen a chemical pollutant in the early atmosphere of Earth?

_____

_____

_____

_____

2. How does the ozone layer protect life on Earth?

_____

_____

_____

_____

_____

3. Describe how fractional distillation is used in the production of oxygen.

_____

_____

_____

4. How does the introduction of oxygen into molten iron and scrap remove impurities?

_____

_____

_____

_____

5. Why is it important to cool the hot water produced in industrial processes before returning it to streams and lakes?

_____

_____

_____

_____

Sulfur: Using Earth's Yellow Mineral

A trip to Old Faithful at Yellowstone Park or Colorado's Pagosa Springs will bring you up close to one of sulfur's more powerful characteristics — smell. Hikers sometimes sprinkle powdered sulfur around their ankles and waists because chiggers and ticks don't like the taste. The pungent smell people associate with sulfur is actually the odor of hydrogen sulfide, a poisonous gas responsible for the stench of rotten eggs. Eggs emit a strong odor when organic, sulfur-containing substances in them are allowed to decay, producing hydrogen sulfide. This gas is also called stinkdamp. After a year in chemistry, you will probably be familiar with the pungent smell of sulfur compounds!

Sulfur makes up less than 0.1 percent of Earth's crust and is frequently found as a free element in volcanic regions and areas of hot mineral springs. Texas and Louisiana possess the distinction of having the largest free sulfur deposits in the world; 80 percent of the world's supply is mined in these two states. Sulfur is typically found over salt domes in limestone and in caprock formations. The chemically combined forms of sulfur exist primarily as sulfate and sulfite hydrates such as gypsum (calcium sulfate dihydrate, $CaSO_4 \cdot 2H_2O$), Epsom salt (magnesium sulfate heptahydrate, $MgSO_4 \cdot 7H_2O$), and glauber salt (sodium sulfate decahydrate, $Na_2SO_4 \cdot 10H_2O$). Epsom and glauber salts are generally found in mineral springs. In addition, sulfur is found in these minerals: galena (PbS), zinc blende (ZnS), chalcopyrite ($CuFeS_2$), and cinnabar (HgS). It also occurs in some plants and animals as constituents of garlic, cabbage, mustard, eggs, horseradish, wool, and hair.

Sulfur Production

The elemental sulfur in Texas and Louisiana is extracted by the Frasch process, which is somewhat like the process used in drilling for oil. A hole is bored from the surface to the deposit, and three pipes are lowered into the ore bed 60 to 600 meters deep (see Figure 1).

Superheated water (74 to 165°C) is forced down the largest pipe, where it melts the sulfur, which has a low melting point. Compressed hot air is pumped down a smaller pipe, and a frothy mixture of molten sulfur, water, and air is forced to the surface through the third pipe. This process yields sulfur that is approximately 99.5 percent pure.

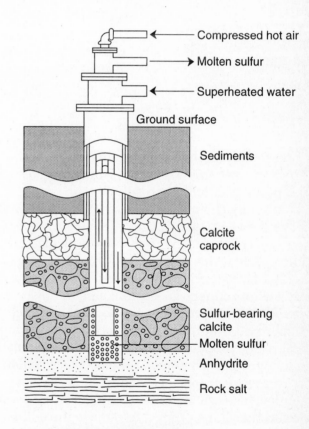

Labels: Compressed hot air — Molten sulfur — Superheated water — Ground surface — Sediments — Calcite caprock — Sulfur-bearing calcite — Molten sulfur — Anhydrite — Rock salt

Frasch Process for Mining Sulfur
Figure 1

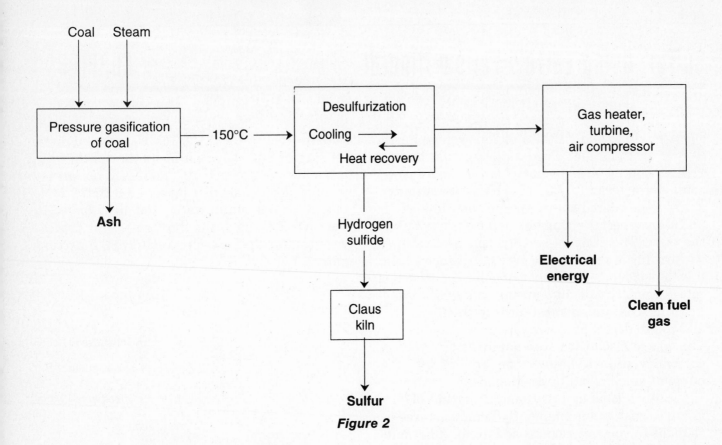

Figure 2

A second method of obtaining sulfur is the Claus process (see Figure 2), which involves partial burning of hydrogen sulfide (H_2S), a byproduct of many chemical processes, to produce sulfur dioxide (SO_2). The SO_2 and the remaining H_2S then react with each other to produce elemental sulfur. The Claus method, or a modification of it, is used for removing sulfur from natural gas, petroleum refinery gases, and smelter gases. Smelters are plants that produce metals such as copper and iron from impure ores. Synthetic natural gas is produced through use of a coal gasification process when natural gas is not available in an area. Europe—Germany, in particular—has developed gasification techniques that incorporate the Claus process to remove the sulfur from poor-quality coal. This is an efficient method of fuel production that yields clean fuel. Four million tons of sulfur are recovered each year using this technique, which converts sulfur from its combined form, as an atmospheric pollutant, to a useful and marketable element.

Uses

Ninety percent of all sulfur is used in making sulfuric acid (H_2SO_4). This compound is the single most important industrial chemical used today. Sulfuric acid is used in making fertilizers, iron and steel, various petroleum products, and industrial chemicals. Carbon disulfide, a solvent, is used in the production of rayon and synthetic films. Sulfur compounds are also used in gunpowder and matches, fungicides, the so-called sulfa drugs, lime-sulfur sprays used to destroy plant parasites, and the production of paper.

In 1839, Charles Goodyear accidentally discovered that the addition of sulfur to rubber during heating—a process now called vulcanization—decreased the tendency of the rubber to become tacky (sticky) in warm weather and brittle in cold weather. The resulting rubber is much tougher, and products made from it last longer. Although some tires are styrene-butadiene synthetic rubber, most of the tires in North America are now natural rubber because bias-ply tires have been replaced by radials. An advantage of natural rubber tires is that the rubber can be recovered and recycled.

Environmental Concerns About Sulfur

Coal-powered electric plants produce polluting gaseous emissions caused by the presence of sulfur in the coal they burn. Sulfur dioxide gas is a byproduct of the combustion of coal and produces acid rain when it combines with water vapor in the atmosphere. Hard coal (anthracite) is low in sulfur, whereas soft coal (bituminous) contains greater amounts of that element. Bituminous coal is much cheaper and more available in some areas, so electric utility companies opt to use it in power plants, but they must then be willing to tackle the resulting sulfur problem. Most coal-powered electric plants remove sulfur from the emitted gases by means of scrubbers in the smokestacks. Scrubbers remove particulate matter, ash, and some gases from the smoke in the flue produced by the burning of coal. Sulfur dioxide scrubbers spray slurries of lime, or limestone, into the emission gases in the stacks and pass the smoke through a slurry of the limestone and water. The limestone chemically reacts with the sulfur dioxide through a series of reactions to produce sulfurous acid and calcium sulfite. The limestone must be replaced periodically, or the scrubbers become inoperative. The scrubbers can remove up to 95 percent of the sulfur dioxide from flue gases. An average power station will produce several hundred tons of spent slurry every day. Disposal of such huge amounts of waste rapidly becomes a major problem, and research continues for new ways of removing sulfur dioxide.

1. Besides bringing sulfur to the surface, what other benefit does the Frasch process have over most mining techniques that yield ores?

_____

_____

2. Why might a doctor recommend that a traveler going into a mosquito-infested area take sulfa drugs prior to the trip?

_____

_____

_____

3. If scrubbers remove 95 percent of the sulfur dioxide in flue gases, why are environmentalists still concerned about the amount of this gas released into the atmosphere?

_____

_____

_____

4. Why does the Claus method involve only partial burning of hydrogen sulfide?

_____

_____

_____

_____

5. Providers of bottled gas such as propane and methane add tiny amounts of hydrogen sulfide to these gases, which are normally odorless. Why?

_____

_____

_____

_____

6. What is the benefit of adding sulfur to natural rubber during vulcanization?

_____

_____

7. As our petroleum reserves are depleted, low-quality, high-sulfur petroleum will become more important. Desulfurization is therefore a research topic of some concern now. Why?

_____

_____

_____

_____

The Making of Ammonia

The pungent gas ammonia takes its name from the Ammonians. These ancient worshippers of the Egyptian god Amun used *sal volatile* (ammonium chloride) in their religious rites. During the Middle Ages, ammonia was used in the dyeing of woolen goods and in tanning. This colorless gas is generally thought of as nonflammable but will burn in air under some conditions. It dissolves readily in water because it interacts with water molecules. The fact that ammonia is extremely soluble in water is what makes its presence so obvious to your nose. It dissolves in the aqueous mucus that coats the olfactory tissue of the nose. Water might smell just as pungent if our nasal sensors were not constantly saturated with it!

At the beginning of the twentieth century, prominent scientists were warning of approaching world famine because of a scarcity of fertilizer containing nitrogen. The nitrogen is needed by plants to make proteins. Some types of bacteria "fix" nitrogen from the air, forming nitrates, which plants can use. But large-scale farming requires more abundant nitrates, which can be made from ammonia. However, because ammonia could not be produced in abundance, most nitrates had to be imported from mined deposits, mainly in Chile.

Nitrates are also used in the manufacture of explosives. In 1913, as World War I was approaching, Germany was under pressure to obtain ammonia needed to make such explosives. These factors led researchers to investigate methods of producing ammonia on an industrial scale. Fritz Haber, a German chemist, learned

that ammonia could be produced by the direct combination of nitrogen from the air and hydrogen through the following reaction:

$$N_2(g) + 3H_2(g) \rightleftarrows 2NH_3(g)$$

To occur at a reasonable rate, the reaction requires the presence of a catalyst, high temperature, and high pressure. Because the reaction is reversible, the ammonia must be removed as it is produced to keep the reaction moving to the right, in favor of the product. Karl Bosch, an engineer from a German company interested in Haber's work, designed equipment that could operate at temperatures up to 550°C and up to 200 atmospheres, making the large-scale production of ammonia possible. The process developed to produce ammonia is known as the Haber-Bosch process.

Today, ammonia ranks as one of the most important industrial substances. Modern chemical plants that produce ammonia manufacture thousands of tons per day. The ammonia is then used in the manufacture of explosives, plastics, soap, and many other common products. However, the greatest percentage of ammonia is used in the production of fertilizers. The nitrogen in fertilizers is supplied directly or indirectly by ammonia. Fertilizers replenish nitrogen and other substances, particularly potassium and phosphorus, that have been reduced or exhausted in soils.

Ammonia is used as a fertilizer in both gaseous and liquid form. The gas is pumped directly into the soil. The liquid form, called anhydrous ammonia, is also added directly to the soil. Plants are able to absorb some of the ammonia, using it to make proteins. Bacteria in the soil convert much of the ammonia to nitrites (NO_2^-) and then to nitrates (NO_3^-). Plants absorb the nitrates and also utilize the source of nitrogen in making proteins.

Many commercial fertilizers supply nitrogen in the form of nitrate salts that are manufactured from nitric acid, HNO_3. Here again, ammonia plays a role because nitric acid is produced from ammonia from a method called the Ostwald process. In the Ostwald process, ammonia reacts with oxygen in the presence of a platinum-rhodium catalyst to yield nitrogen monoxide. The equation for the reaction is as follows.

$$4NH_3(g) + 5O_2(g) \rightarrow 4NO(g) + 6H_2O(g)$$

The NO produced then reacts with oxygen to form nitrogen dioxide.

$$2NO(g) + O_2(g) \rightarrow 2NO_2(g)$$

When NO_2 is combined with water, and the mixture is further processed, nearly pure nitric acid is produced. To produce high-nitrogen fertilizer, nitric acid can be reacted with ammonia to produce ammonium nitrate, NH_4NO_3, an important fertilizer. Nitric acid is also used to produce metallic salts, such as potassium nitrate (KNO_3). Such salts are important ingredients in many fertilizers.

Fertilizers can be used to tailor soils for specific crops, to enrich poor soils, and to increase crop yield. However, runoff is a problem with these fertilizers because they are highly soluble in water. Contamination of bodies of water by nitrogen fertilizers is a serious form of pollution. Increased plant growth in the affected body of water can lead to oxygen depletion and the "death" of the body of water. Controlled-release fertilizers are under development, but are currently used only in nonfarming applications, due to their cost.

1. What factors led to investigation of methods for producing ammonia on a large scale?

   _____

   _____

2. Describe the Haber-Bosch process for producing ammonia.

   _____

   _____

3. Explain why ammonia is important in large-scale farming for food production.

   _____

   _____

   _____

4. Why is ammonia such an important chemical material?

   _____

   _____

5. What effect does fertilizer runoff have on bodies of water?

   _____

   _____

6. How does the concept of equilibrium relate to the fact that ammonia must be removed during the Haber-Bosch process if the reaction is to continue?

   _____

   _____

   _____

Synthetic Gems: The Making of All That Glitters

 ems have long been valued for their beauty and hardness. For thousands of years, they have been used as jewelry. Only since the start of the industrial age have such precious stones as diamonds, rubies, and sapphires been sought for their use in various manufacturing processes. In order to meet this growing demand, scientists have looked for ways to create synthetic gems.

Most gemstones are minerals with crystalline structures. Most are also extremely hard; that is, they are resistant to being scratched. On a hardness scale of 1 (softest) to 10 (hardest), diamonds rank 10, and rubies and sapphires 9. These three kinds of gems also are very tough, which means they are resistant to cleavage and fracture.

Diamond, the transparent allotrope of carbon, is probably the most important gemstone, both for decorative and industrial use. Ruby and sapphire are both varieties of the mineral corundum, a form of aluminum oxide. Ruby is corundum that is orange-red to violet red; all other colors of corundum are classified as sapphire. Thus, although sapphires are best known in their blue form, colorless, pink, and yellow sapphires also exist.

Synthetic gems must be identical to the corresponding naturally occurring minerals. They must have the same appearance, chemical composition, crystal structure, hardness, and optical properties, including color and brilliancy. Some gems exhibit special optical phenomena, such as the star effect that can be seen in many sapphires, and these also must be duplicated when necessary.

The search for ways to produce synthetic gems dates back to the 19th century, but it was not until 1902 that French chemist Auguste Verneuil announced the successful production of a synthetic ruby of gem quality. The Verneuil process, shown in Figure 1, is also called the flame-fusion method because it uses the high temperatures of the flame produced by burning hydrogen in pure oxygen. To produce ruby by this method, powdered chromium(III) oxide (Cr_2O_3) is added to highly pure powdered corundum (Al_2O_3). The intense heat of the flame fuses the powder into droplets of synthetic ruby, which is basically aluminum oxide with chromium incorporated into the crystal. It is the chromium that gives the ruby its red color.

Figure 1

Verneuil Method

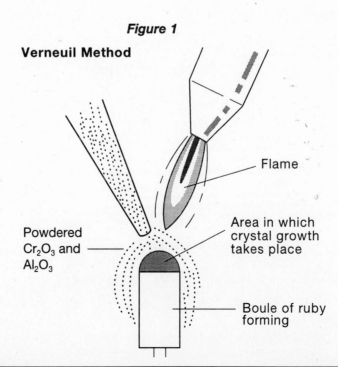

Powdered
Cr_2O_3 and
Al_2O_3

Flame

Area in which
crystal growth
takes place

Boule of ruby
forming

As the droplets of ruby harden in the Verneuil process, more chromium oxide and corundum are added. Eventually, a cylindrical mass, called a boule, is formed. The typical boule is 1.27 cm in diameter and 2.54 – 5.08 cm long. If corundum alone is used in the process, a boule of colorless sapphire is produced.

Synthetic gems also can be produced by means of the Bridgman-Stockbarger method, illustrated in Figure 2. In this method, minerals are placed in a cylindrical crucible with a conical bottom. The crucible is heated and then slowly lowered, bottom first, into a cooler area of the heating apparatus. The crystal forms in the conical area at the bottom of the crucible.

Figure 2

Bridgman-Stockbarger Method

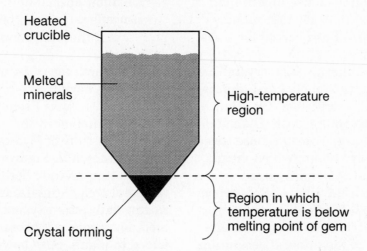

The Czochralski method, also known as the crystal-pulling method, is illustrated in Figure 3. It makes use of seed crystals. Minerals are melted in a crucible that is placed in such a way that the temperature can be decreased quickly just above the surface of the liquefied mass. A seed crystal is lowered into the crucible until it just touches the top surface of the melt. Crystals begin to grow on the bottom of the seed, which then is slowly lifted upward. Crystal growth continues to take place at the bottom of the resulting crystal. This method is widely used to manufacture crystals large enough for use in semiconductors such as transistors and diodes.

Figure 3

Czochralski Method

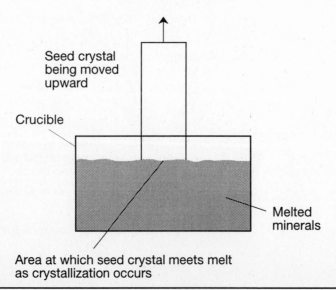

The Bridgman-Stockbarger method and the Czochralski method are referred to as conservative methods because, in each case, the amount of material in the system is not altered during the crystal-producing process. The Verneuil method is nonconservative because new mineral powder must be added during the process.

Other ways of manufacturing crystals include flux fusion and the hydrothermal process. Flux fusion involves the melting of minerals that have relatively low melting points; slow cooling of the melt causes crystallization to occur. In the hydrothermal process, crystals are slowly grown in aqueous solutions. This process is used most for the making of synthetic emeralds, which are crystals of beryl, a compound of beryllium that has the formula $3BeO \cdot Al_2O_3 \cdot 6SiO_2$. Chromium impurities in the crystals produce the green color that is characteristic of emeralds.

Synthetic gems are very important for modern industry. Because of their toughness, sapphires and rubies are used mainly to make long-lasting bearings in watches, meters, and other small mechanical devices. Because of their cheapness and availability, synthetic rubies and sapphires have completely replaced natural ones for these uses. Synthetic quartz, because of its crystalline structure and the way in which the atoms in it vibrate, is used to maintain exact

frequencies in radio transmission and reception as well as in telephone and radar use.

Diamond has proven to be among the most difficult gems to synthesize. None were produced synthetically until 1955, when scientists at the General Electric Company made small, industrial-quality diamonds, using a brute-force process that required very high pressure and temperature. To speed up the reaction, a metal such as iron or nickel was added. By 1970, General Electric scientists were able to synthesize small gem-quality diamonds. Most synthetic diamonds produced in this and other processes are ground up to make diamond grit, an extremely efficient polishing agent.

When synthetic gems were first introduced, it was generally believed that they would lower the value of natural gems. Oddly enough, this has not been the case. The value of most natural gemstones, in fact, has continued to increase since Verneuil perfected his process; people still seem willing to pay a premium in order to buy "the real thing." However, because of their availability and relative cheapness, synthetic gems have lowered the prices of the manufactured goods in which natural gems were once used. Many of today's wristwatches, radios, and telephones, for example, would be far more expensive if synthetic gemstones were not available.

1. What does it mean to say that an object, such as a gemstone, is crystalline?

_____

_____

_____

2. What are two important characteristics that diamonds, rubies, and sapphires all possess?

_____

_____

_____

3. In what way are rubies and sapphires alike? In what way are they different?

_____

_____

_____

4. In the Verneuil process, what materials are fused to produce synthetic rubies?

_____

_____

_____

5. What is the most common process used for making synthetic emeralds?

_____

_____

6. How are most synthetic rubies and sapphires used industrially?

_____

_____

_____

7. Carbon atoms in diamonds are in a three-dimensional arrangement in which each carbon is bonded covalently to four other carbons in a tetrahedron. What is this type of crystal called? How does this arrangement contribute to diamond's hardness and high melting point?

_____

_____

_____

_____

_____

_____

Glass: Is It Really Only Melted Sand?

From the beauty of stained glass to the usefulness of fiberglass optics, from the precision of a telescope lens to the simplicity of a window pane, glass is one of the most widespread materials, and the glassmaking industry one of the most far-reaching. The main ingredient of glass is silica, or sand (SiO_2), and its unique characteristics are based on the chemistry of the Group 14 element silicon.

According to legend, glass was discovered by ancient people when a hot campfire, left burning overnight, heated the sand underneath to the melting point; it is claimed that, upon cooling, a primitive chunk of glass was found. It is more likely, however, that glassmaking was first discovered around 7000 B.C. in the ancient Near East, when sand containing calcium carbonate and sodium carbonate was present as an impurity in clay pottery being readied for firing. Then, a chance overheating of the kiln could have resulted in the formation of glass. It was probably around 1500 B.C. when a clever potter produced the first glass holloware by heating a mixture of sand, soda ash, and lime to a very high temperature, using a rod to hollow out the partially cooled glob of glass that resulted. The first factory in America was a glasshouse, begun one year after the founding of Jamestown in 1607. It was, however, doomed by the hardships of the New World and the unwillingness of most of the fashionable settlers to work. It closed in 1609 but has been restored and is now open again.

Glassmaking began to flourish as an American industry around the middle of the eighteenth century with such factories as the Wistarberg Works in New Jersey, which emphasized utilitarian soda-lime glass, and the Mannheim Works in Pennsylvania, which produced clear (and expensive) flint glass. However, it was not until the beginning of the twentieth century that glass manufacture was approached as a science in response to the need for high-quality optical instruments.

As at the beginning, today's glassmaking is founded on silicon in the form of silica. Like carbon in the same family, silicon can form covalent bonds by sharing electrons. Silica and the complex silicates are formed with silicon-oxygen linkages in the silicate ion. The negative silicate ion (SiO_4^{4-}), forms a tetrahedron that can share oxygen molecules in other tetrahedrons to form giant negative ions. This structure leads to a great variety of silicate minerals, including quartz (crystalline silica). The tetrahedral arrangement produces very rigid structures, with oxygen atoms shared by two silicon atoms.

These properties of silica—its rigid molecular structure and its ability to form extended molecules—enable it to form glass under the right conditions. The unusual properties of glass, including its smoothness and transparency or translucence, are due to the formation of the silica into a noncrystalline amorphous material. After silica is melted, slow cooling results in recrystallization, but more rapid cooling produces glass. In terms of atomic arrangement, glass may be considered liquid silica with a viscosity so high that it behaves like a solid. In practice, most glassmaking adds such materials as oxides of either alkali or alkaline earth metals, which react with the SiO_2 melt. Such additives convert some of the Si-O-Si links into terminal Si-O⁻ groups; this structure partially disrupts the Si-O network and results in a lower working temperature. Figure 1 on the next page shows several silica structures.

Although silica is the major ingredient of most glass, the types and percentages of additives determine the nature of the glass that results. Today's manufacturers are able to produce a huge variety of glass for many uses. The major families of glass and their components in addition to silica are as follows.

1. Soda-lime is composed of soda (Na_2O) or sodium carbonate (Na_2CO_3), which acts as a dissolving agent, or flux, for the silica; lime (CaO) or calcium carbonate ($CaCO_3$), which stabilizes glass; and other oxides. This kind of glass is the most common and is inexpensive and strong.

2. Lead crystal is glass in which lead oxide (PbO) replaces lime and part of the silica. This glass

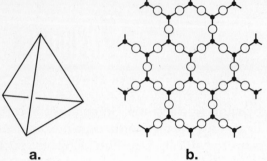

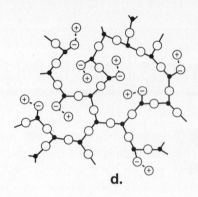

Figure 1

Key
- ● silicon atom
- ○ oxygen atom
- ⊕ sodium ion

Silica Structures
a. Basic tetrahedral shape
b. Crystalline silica (two-dimensional)
c. Fused silica glass (two-dimensional)
d. Soda-lime glass (two dimensional)

softens at low temperatures and is easy to work with. The high electron density of the lead gives the glass a high index of refraction, which results in its fine optical qualities.

3. Borosilicate glass contains boric oxide (B_2O_3) and a small amount of alkali oxide. The boron atoms aligned in Si–O–B bonds result in a side-to-side vibration that gives excellent heat-resistance. This is the least expensive heat-resistant glass.

4. Fused silica, or vitreous glass contains no additives. It is extremely resistant to thermal shock and chemical attack and transmits ultraviolet and infrared rays with a lower energy loss than does any other glass. However, it requires a high temperature and vacuum for manufacture and is very expensive.

5. Vycor-96% silica glass is a borosilicate glass that has been specially treated to become very heat resistant.

6. Aluminosilicate glass contains aluminum oxide (Al_2O_3). This glass also resists high temperatures.

7. Optical and colored glasses are made with a variety of additives.

Most modern glass manufacture follows a standard procedure. The ingredients are thoroughly mixed, with the addition of varying amounts of cullet (pieces of waste or recycled glass), which causes the sand to melt at lower temperatures. The ingredients are then melted in a large furnace at 1400°–1500°C, the temperature is reduced to 900°–1200°C, and the molten glass is formed into desired shapes. Figure 2 shows a typical tank furnace for glassmaking.

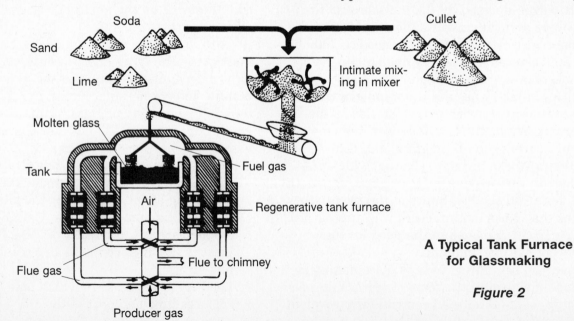

A Typical Tank Furnace for Glassmaking

Figure 2

Most oven materials would dissolve in the molten silicates, so the tanks usually are lined with fused alumina (Al_2O_3). The furnaces are heated with gas or oil; energy is conserved by the use of heat exchangers, which typically raise the temperature of the gas and air before these materials enter the furnace. The furnace operates continuously; operation never shuts down until the lining has to be replaced, at intervals ranging from every 10 to 20 months to every 8 to 10 years.

A variety of shaping methods are used. Bottles are made by a process called blow-molding (see Figure 3), in which molten glass is placed in a mold and blown out into it with compressed air until the glass takes the shape of the mold.

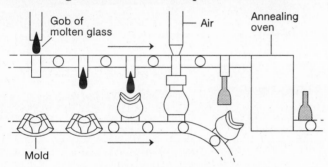

Blow-Molding of Glass Bottles

Figure 3

Window and other plate glass is made by the float process, introduced in 1959. In this process, molten glass leaves the furnace in a wide ribbon and floats on a bath of melted tin. This process takes place in a nitrogen atmosphere, rather than in air, and results in a flat glass with parallel sides that do not need polishing. Other

shaping methods include casting, rolling, pressing, spinning, and molding. Afterward, the final product may be further cut, milled, ground, polished, etched, or painted.

Glass manufacture is a large and important industry that produces a tremendous variety of materials. It is also an industry upon which many other industries depend. These industries may require glass containers for their products, glass lenses to check quality, glass heat and electrical insulation, glass for lighting, and glass windows to protect the plant itself from the weather.

The industry is not free from problems, but glass manufacture is generally a clean process with few toxic by-products. The main environmental concern is that it is an energy-intensive process and consumes a large amount of fuel. The fuel, however, is usually natural gas, which emits no particulate pollution. Attempts to conserve energy include the use of continuous melting tanks with heat exchangers and the use of cullet to lower the required temperature. Current research is exploring methods that use complex metal oxides to further lower the heat required. Another area of possible harm to the environment is the discharge of hot water into streams. However, water is used for cooling only when the tank is drained for relining, and with newer tanks this process is necessary only every few years. The fact that glass is highly recyclable, with up to 80 percent of the melt being former waste glass, is also a benefit.

1. Draw an electron dot structure for the silicate ion ($SiO_4{}^{4-}$). Distinguish between electrons of Si and of O and those that have come from the corresponding positive ions in the compound.

2. What special problem is encountered by the manufacturers of the ovens used in glassmaking?

_____

_____

_____

3. A supercooled liquid is one that has been cooled so fast that it does not change from the liquid state to its normal crystalline solid form. Explain why glass may be considered a supercooled liquid.

_____

_____

_____

4. What type of glass might be most useful in biological studies that require ultraviolet light?

_____

_____

_____

5. Name two major industries that could not exist without glass, and give two or more examples of glass products used by them.

_____

_____

_____

6. Suggest one or more possible hazards to workers in glass manufacturing.

_____

_____

_____

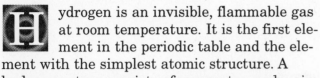

Hydrogen: More Than Just the "H" In H₂O

CHAPTER 9

Use with Section 9.1

Hydrogen is an invisible, flammable gas at room temperature. It is the first element in the periodic table and the element with the simplest atomic structure. A hydrogen atom consists of one proton and a single electron. The most abundant element in the universe, hydrogen makes up more than 90 percent of all the atoms and three-quarters of all the mass that exists. Hydrogen is the fuel that powers the sun. The heat at the center of the sun, estimated to be as high as 10 million degrees Celsius, causes hydrogen atoms to fuse together, releasing huge amounts of energy.

If conditions are cold enough, gaseous hydrogen can turn into a liquid or even into a metal. There is evidence that in the interior of the planet Jupiter, for instance, freezing temperatures and intense pressure convert hydrogen into a metal. As the solid hydrogen remelts, the resulting liquid hydrogen oozes upward, just as lava does from Earth's volcanoes.

The name "hydrogen" was suggested in 1781 by the French chemist Antoine Lavoisier, who derived it from the Greek words *hydro*, meaning "water," and *genes*, meaning "forming." Thus, *hydrogen* means "water-forming." In fact, two hydrogen atoms combine with one oxygen atom to form water. It is through its presence in acids that hydrogen was first discovered in the 16th

century by the Swiss physician Philippus Paracelsus. At the time, however, it was not recognized as an element and was confused with other combustible gases, such as carbon monoxide. In 1766, the English chemist Henry Cavendish showed that hydrogen is an element. Cavendish measured hydrogen's density and the volume of hydrogen gas released by a given amount of acid that reacted with a metal. He called this hydrogen gas "inflammable air." Hydrogen burns in air and reacts explosively with oxygen to produce water.

On Earth, elemental hydrogen exists as molecules composed of two hydrogen atoms. The two atoms of hydrogen are joined by a single covalent bond, and each atom has a stable configuration. Although hydrogen is the ninth-most-abundant element on Earth, it makes up less than one percent of the weight of Earth's crust.

The most important naturally occurring compound of hydrogen is water. Hydrogen is also present in all animal and plant matter, usually combined with carbon. Hydrocarbons, compounds of carbon and hydrogen, are constituents of petroleum and coal, which are called fossil fuels. Hydrogen gas is also found buried in deposits of salt or coal. Free hydrogen is sometimes ejected as a gas from volcanoes.

Figure 1

Hydrogen Molecule

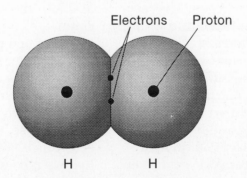

Electrons   Proton

H   H

In 1932, the American chemist Harold Urey found a natural isotope of hydrogen that had a neutron in its nucleus. He called it deuterium. Deuterium is an important research tool, used to make heavy water (deuterium oxide), which is used in nuclear reactors to control the fission reaction by absorbing neutrons. In 1935, British scientists made another isotope of hydrogen. This one had two neutrons in its nucleus. They called it tritium. You will read more about these isotopes in Chapter 21.

Figure 2

Isotopes of Hydrogen

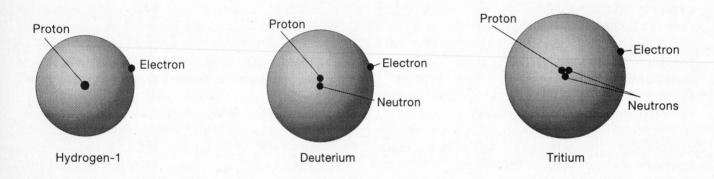

Hydrogen-1   Deuterium   Tritium

Hydrogen is usually prepared in the laboratory by the action of dilute acids on metals. Another common method used to produce hydrogen in the laboratory is the decomposition of water by means of an electric current.

Hydrogen is manufactured commercially by the reaction of steam with white-hot carbon or by a similar process that uses a nickel catalyst and hydrocarbons in place of carbon. Hydrogen is a by-product of the production of hydrocarbon fuels from petroleum. The production of hydrogen in the United States amounts to hundreds of millions of cubic feet of the gas per day.

Today, enormous quantities of hydrogen are employed in a variety of processes. The synthesis of ammonia is a major use of hydrogen. The reaction involves the direct combination of nitrogen from the air with hydrogen. Ammonia is used in the manufacture of many important nitrogen-containing compounds, including nitric acid, urea, and such fertilizers as ammonium nitrate.

Large amounts of hydrogen are used in the production of hydrogen chloride and hydrochloric acid. Hydrogen and chlorine react to form hydrogen chloride, which forms hydrochloric acid when dissolved in water. The manufacture of many organic compounds also involves the use of hydrogen. For example, methanol is synthesized when carbon monoxide reacts with hydrogen at a temperature of 400°C and a pressure of 300 atmospheres in the presence of zinc oxide and chromium oxide. Hydrogen is used in the extraction of certain metals, such as molybdenum and tungsten, from their oxides, in the manufacture of special metal castings, and in the production of magnesium. Hydrogen is also used to cool large electric generators.

Liquid hydrogen has important applications in cryogenics, low-temperature studies of the behavior of matter. It is also used in the study of low-temperature superconductivity because its melting point is only a few degrees above absolute zero. Liquid hydrogen is used in bubble chambers for photographing the tracks of nuclear particles and for their identification.

Large quantities of liquid hydrogen have been used in space research both as a fuel for generating electric power in fuel cells and as a rocket fuel with oxygen or fluorine as the oxidizer. For this purpose, a mixture of liquid and solid hydrogen, which forms a slush, is preferred to liquid hydrogen because the mixture has a lower temperature, higher density, and greater stability.

In the quest for new and improved energy sources and uses, there is interest in employing hydrogen as an energy source. Fuels would be used to produce electricity, which would be used to produce hydrogen from water. The hydrogen would be stored as a liquid and subsequently burned to release the stored energy when needed.

Hydrogenation is an important reaction in organic chemistry in which hydrogen is added to another substance—generally a compound containing double bonds—usually by means of a catalyst. Various animal and vegetable oils (fish, soybean, and peanut) are converted by hydrogenation to solid fats with consistencies more suitable for margarine, soaps, shortenings, and other edible and industrial products. Coal, petroleum, and tar are hydrogenated to convert solid fuels or heavy oils into more usable liquid fuels.

A peroxide is a chemical compound in which there are two linked oxygen atoms. Several hundred peroxy compounds are known, of which a few dozen have commercial value. The best-known and most widely used peroxy compound is hydrogen peroxide (H_2O_2), sometimes written as HOOH to indicate the structure. Hydrogen peroxide was discovered in 1818 by Louis Jacques Thenard. It is a colorless liquid that freezes at about the same temperature as water. Extremely pure preparations are stable, but even trace contaminants cause hydrogen peroxide to decompose, producing oxygen.

Because hydrogen peroxide releases oxygen, it has been used in rockets to supply oxygen to burn fuel. Hydrogen peroxide is also valuable as a bleaching agent. Of all the hydrogen peroxide produced commercially, about 70 percent is used to bleach natural and synthetic fibers and paper.

1. What properties would have caused early researchers to name hydrogen "inflammable air"?

   _____

   _____

   _____

   _____

2. Describe hydrogen's atomic structure and its molecular structure.

   _____

   _____

   _____

   _____

3. Compare the ways that hydrogen is made in the laboratory with the ways that it is produced commercially.

   _____

   _____

   _____

   _____

4. Describe some industrial uses of hydrogen.

_____

_____

_____

_____

_____

5. List several uses for liquid hydrogen.

_____

_____

_____

_____

_____

_____

Soaps and Detergents: A Very "Clean" Industry   CHAPTER 13

housands of different types and brands of cleansers exist on the market today. There are specialty cleaners for counter tops, woods, upholstery, porcelain, cookware, clothing, cars, and people. These cleansers include soaps and detergents. Although soaps have been used for several thousand years, detergents were not developed until the 1950s.

Soaps and detergents act as surfactants. Surfactants are substances that have a hydrophobic (water-fearing) end and a hydrophilic (water-loving) end. The hydrophilic end allows the compound to dissolve or disperse in water. The hydrophobic end dissolves grease, dirt, and various organic substances, including fats, that do not dissolve in water. Fats are hydrophobic molecules. Such nonpolar molecules do not form hydrogen bonds with water. As a consequence, fats, including grease, do not dissolve in water.

A molecule of soap or detergent is made from a fatty acid, which has a nonpolar hydrocarbon tail and a polar head. The nonpolar end of a fatty acid readily loses a hydrogen ion and becomes negatively charged. By chemically combining with a positive metal ion, such as sodium, to form a salt, the fatty acid becomes a soap. In water, the soap releases the fatty acid as a negative ion. The nonpolar hydrocarbon tail becomes embedded in fat globules. The polar head of the fatty acid sticks out into the water. As a result, the surface of a grease droplet becomes covered with a sheath made up of the polar ends of the fatty acid. These polar ends do not dissolve in the grease, but they form hydrogen bonds with water. With mechanical agitation, the fat globule is dispersed in the water solution and is rinsed away.

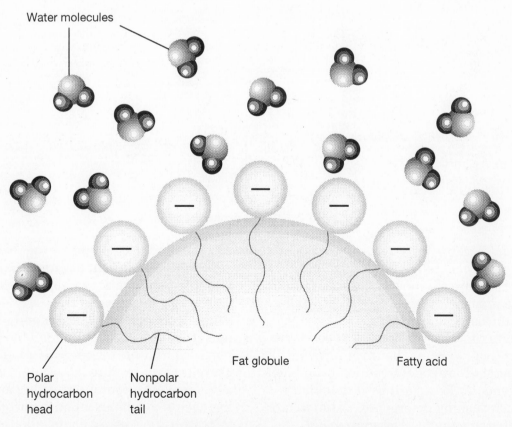

Water molecules

Polar hydrocarbon head

Nonpolar hydrocarbon tail

Fat globule   Fatty acid

Figure 1 **Grease Droplet Covered with Fatty Acids**

The basic process of making soap is called *saponification*. Fat reacts with alkali, such as potassium hydroxide, to form soap and glycerol. The mixture is then rinsed to remove the glycerol. In earlier times, people made soap in a kettle. They boiled animal fat and wood ashes for several hours in the kettle. The modern version of this method uses a kettle with a capacity of 25 000 to 140 000 kg and is designed for heating, settling, and blending the fats, alkali, salt, and water.

Another method for producing soap is the *hydrolyzer process*. In hydrolysis, fat and water react to form fatty acid and glycerol. The reaction actually takes place in steps, forming intermediate glycerides. In order for hydrolysis to occur, water and fat molecules must be in direct contact. This contact is made possible by high temperatures that promote dissolving of water in the fat phase. Fat or water is added or glycerol is removed as the process occurs. A zinc oxide catalyst is used to increase the rate of reaction. Distillation of the soap is the second step, removing water and fatty acid vapors and maintaining good odor and color in the finished product. The final steps involve hardening to improve the physical characteristics of the soap, including its moisturizing abilities. The final product is usually called neat soap. Neat soap contains about 69 percent actual soap and 30 percent water. The remaining portion is sodium chloride and other stabilizers. The hydrolyzer process produces better-quality soap and provides a simplified method of glycerol removal. One hydrolyzer unit produces as much soap as 10 kettles are able to produce.

Most water is hard to some extent, meaning that it contains dissolved minerals such as calcium and magnesium compounds. Soaps produce a precipitate with the calcium and magnesium ions present in hard water. Detergents do not. This precipitate, called lime soap, is responsible for

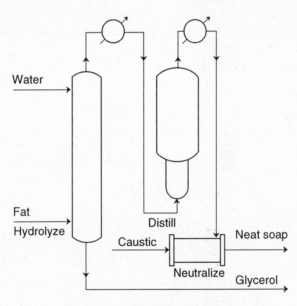

Figure 2   **The Hydrolysis Process**

bathtub rings. Because they do not form precipitates, detergents generally are used for the heavy-duty cleaning of laundry, floors, and woodwork, whereas soaps are used for mild cleaning and personal cleansing products.

Detergents contain "builders" that serve to bind dissolved metal ions. The three primary forms of detergent are anionic, cationic, and nonionic detergents. Anionics are used in laundry and hand dishwashing detergents. Cationics are specialty detergent products used in metal cleaners and textile laundering. Nonionic detergents are used in laundry and automatic dishwashing detergents and have low sudsing characteristics. Phosphates may be added to detergents to prevent the calcium and magnesium ions from forming a scum, and to attach to dirt particles that have been washed off the fabric to prevent them from redepositing. Laundry detergents may also contain additives such as bleaching agents to whiten laundry, corrosion inhibitors to protect the washer drum, alkalinity boosters to remove soils that are sensitive to high pH, and sudsing modifiers to make the product more aesthetically pleasing. In addition, brighteners, which are fluorescent dyes that absorb some ultraviolet light and reemit it as visible light, are added to make washed fabrics look brighter. Enzymes produced by bacteria are added to assist in removal of protein and carbohydrate-based stains such as blood, food, grass, and body oils. Some detergents also contain softeners and antistatic substances.

Detergents make up the largest portion of the cleaner market. Among these items, laundry products represent the largest single use, followed by hard-surface cleaners such as dishwashing products, wall cleaners, and abrasive scouring cleansers. In personal-care lines, detergents are used in shampoo, bubble bath, cosmetic cleansers, and toothpastes. Other uses are in rug and upholstery cleaners, scouring pads, and pet-care products. Detergents are used in industry to scour raw yarn, to clean metals prior to painting or electroplating, for disinfecting and cleaning various products, and in surgical preparation products.

Biodegradability is essential for detergents to ensure that detergent components will be broken down by bacterial action. Nonbiodegradable detergents prevent effective bacterial action in septic tanks and sewage treatment plants and can cause undesirable persistent foaming in rivers. One problem is that detergent wash water (also called gray water) is highly nutritious because the phosphates in detergents act as fertilizers and promote the growth of aquatic plants. When the plants die, microorganisms break down the plants. In the process, oxygen in the water is used up and other living things in the water die. This process is called eutrophication.

1. How do soaps clean oil, grease, and other organic materials?

_____

_____

_____

_____

2. Describe the structure of a soap.

_____

_____

_____

_____

3. Describe the process of saponification.

_____

_____

_____

_____

4. Why would soap be unable to get laundry completely clean in areas with hard water?

_____

_____

_____

_____

_____

Sulfuric Acid: The Mark of a Healthy Economy

CHAPTER **14**

Use with Section 14.2

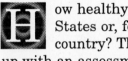 ow healthy is the economy of the United States or, for that matter, any industrial country? There are many ways of coming up with an assessment; the jobless rate, gross national product, company profits, and what's happening to the stock market are a few guidelines that you might use to assess economic stability.

Another indicator of economic health—one that economists have been using for many years–is sulfuric acid production and consumption. Why is it used as such an indicator?

For one thing, sulfuric acid is used in the manufacture of a tremendous number of products that are bought in great quantity when a country has a healthy economy. These products include fertilizers, petroleum, steel, plastics, dyes, drugs, paints, textiles, and a host of substances that are themselves vital to the manufacture of still other products.

As a matter of fact, sulfuric acid is the most massively produced chemical in the world; a whopping 100 million tons or more are churned out yearly worldwide, with the United States contributing about one-third of the total amount produced. In the United States, the largest amount of the acid finds its way into factories that produce phosphate fertilizers, which boost the yields of crops and help put food on our dinner tables.

The value of sulfuric acid has been known for centuries. It was first described around the year 1300 by a Spanish alchemist known by the pseudonym of False Geber. Originally called "oil of vitriol," which refers to its texture (oily) and its composition (sulfate is called vitriol), the acid was first produced commercially in the early 1700s. At first, yields were extremely low and thus, costs were very high. Then, in the mid 1800s, a chemist involved in the manufacture of

Figure 1

The Lead-Chamber Process

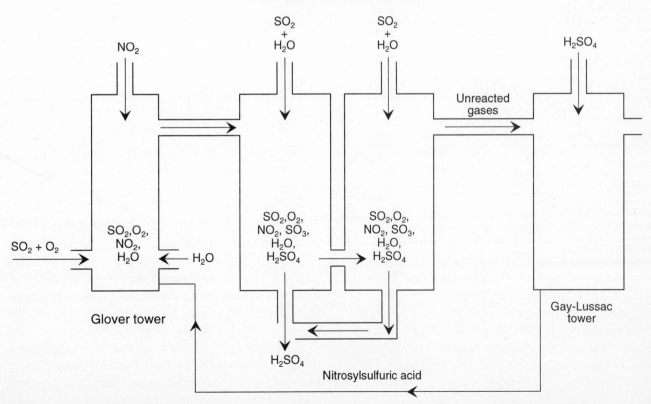

fertilizer, for which sulfuric acid was a vital reagent, hit upon a commercially efficient way of producing the acid in large batches. The process was carried on in large lead chambers and quite naturally came to be called the *lead-chamber process*. Although this process is still used to a limited extent, it is rapidly becoming obsolete.

In general, the raw materials for the lead-chamber process are sulfur dioxide (SO_2), oxygen (O_2) from air, water (H_2O), and nitrogen(IV) oxide (NO_2). These substances are mixed in an initial vessel called a Glover tower (Figure 1). The gas mixture is then passed to a series of lead chambers. Here, the SO_2 and H_2O react with nitrogen dioxide (NO_2), and the resulting sulfur

trioxide (SO_3) reacts with water to form sulfuric acid (H_2SO_4). This sulfuric acid and any remaining reactants are passed on to succeeding chambers. There, more H_2SO_4 is produced by reaction of the NO_2 with newly added SO_2 and H_2O. After passing through the lead chambers, unreacted gases are dissolved in sulfuric acid in a Gay-Lussac tower. The resulting nitrosylsulfuric acid can be recycled back to the Glover tower to make more sulfuric acid.

The lead-chamber process has many variations, but all are relatively inefficient. The process cannot produce concentrations of sulfuric acid greater than 78 percent. This drawback led to the development of more efficient processes,

Figure 2

The Contact Process

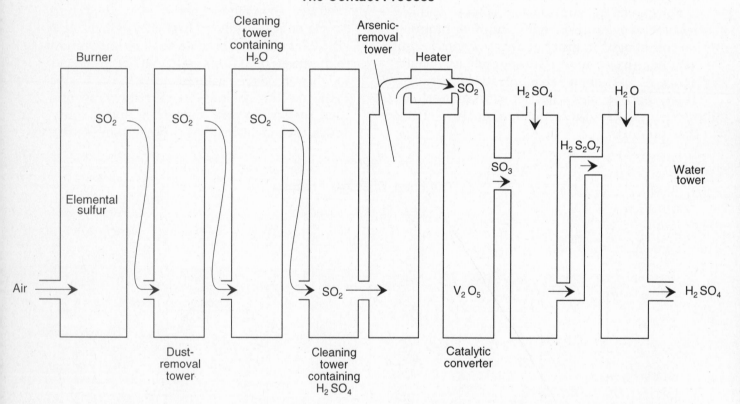

such as the contact process. A number of raw materials can be used to initiate this process. These materials include elemental sulfur, sulfur-containing gases produced as by-products from the smelting of ores such as those of iron and zinc (pyrites), waste acids containing sulfur, and hydrogen sulfide (H_2S). Although the raw material most often used is elemental sulfur, the choice depends largely on such economic factors as the local availability of raw materials.

For example, if an ore-processing plant is located nearby, it makes economic sense to use the waste gases of the smelting process to make sulfuric acid. This usage has the additional advantage of recycling potential air pollutants that would otherwise be vented into the atmosphere at the ore-processing plant.

The contact process works in the following manner. Elemental sulfur or sulfide ores are burned in air. The product, as you might guess, is an oxide of sulfur—in this case, sulfur dioxide (SO_2). The sulfur dioxide is passed through several chambers, where it is cleaned of various impurities such as dust and arsenic (Figure 2). In the presence of air, heat, and the catalyst vanadium pentoxide (V_2O_5) in a catalytic converter, the SO_2 is converted to sulfur trioxide (SO_3) in the following reaction.

$$2SO_2 + O_2 \rightarrow 2SO_3$$

Because this reaction is exothermic and reversible, the amount of SO_3 produced decreases as the temperature increases. As a result, it is advantageous to carry out the reaction at as low a temperature as possible. Practical considerations require that the reaction be run at temperatures between about 450°C and 600°C. That point is the temperature at which V_2O_5 becomes important in the process. At such low temperatures, a catalyst must be used to increase the rate of reaction.

The SO_3 produced is led into a tank containing concentrated sulfuric acid, which absorbs the SO_3. The product, disulfuric, or pyrosulfuric, acid ($H_2S_2O_7$), is made to react with water. Depending on how much water is used, this process can produce sulfuric acid of concentrations up to 100 percent. The sulfuric acid is then shipped in acid-resistant steel tank cars to various consumers.

An interesting by-product of the manufacture of sulfuric acid that is both economically and environmentally beneficial is electricity. All the reactions in the H_2SO_4 production process are exothermic. As a result, a sulfuric acid plant produces an enormous amount of energy. This energy is now recovered in boilers in which water is changed to steam. The steam can then be used to power turbines that turn electric generators. This process of using waste energy from an industrial procedure to generate electricity is an example of cogeneration. In cogeneration, the normally wasted heat energy produced by an industrial process or power plant is used to generate electricity.

1. Explain why the production of sulfuric acid is considered an indicator of a country's economic health.

_____

_____

_____

_____

_____

2. The largest amount of sulfuric acid is used to produce what materials?

_____

_____

_____

3. Which sulfuric acid manufacturing process uses NO_2 as a reactant?

_____

_____

_____

4. Of what environmental benefit is the use of gases from ore-processing plants to produce sulfuric acid?

_____

_____

_____

_____

5. What is the role of vanadium pentoxide in the production of sulfuric acid?

_____

_____

6. Given that H_2SO_4 is called sulfuric acid, what is the name of the ternary acid H_2SO_3? Why is it given that name?

_____

_____

7. Relative to compounds such as H_2SO_4 and H_2SO_3, what are compounds like SO_3 and SO_2 called? Why?

_____

_____

_____

8. What does it mean to say that the acid H_2SO_4 is much stronger than the acid H_2SO_3?

_____

_____

_____

9. What is the relationship between cogeneration and the production of sulfuric acid?

_____

_____

_____

Hydrogen Peroxide: Not Just a Hairdresser's Tool   CHAPTER 16

Hydrogen peroxide (H_2O_2) is a simple molecule made up of two hydrogen atoms and two oxygen atoms. It is similar in composition to water, but the additional oxygen atom greatly changes its chemical properties. Hydrogen peroxide is an important industrial chemical, used in the production of many consumer goods such as paper and textiles. It is supplied in commercial strengths of 3-35 percent by mass. Since it is decomposed easily by heat and light, hydrogen peroxide is stored at comparatively low temperatures in containers that protect it from light.

Commercially, hydrogen peroxide was once

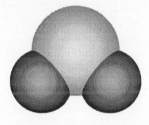

Water

Hydrogen peroxide

Key:

Oxygen atom

Hydrogen atom

produced by electrolysis of aqueous solutions of sulfuric acid and ammonium sulfate. Today, hydrogen peroxide is prepared commercially by the electrolysis of a concentrated solution of sulfuric acid. In the two-step process, the sulfuric acid is first converted to peroxodisulfuric acid ($H_2S_2O_8$) by electrolysis. In the second step, the peroxodisulfuric acid reacts with water to regenerate the sulfuric acid and yield hydrogen peroxide.

In school laboratories, dilute hydrogen peroxide is usually prepared by the reaction between barium peroxide and cold, dilute sulfuric acid. When the resulting insoluble barium sulfate is removed by filtration, a solution of hydrogen peroxide remains.

Peroxides are unwanted products of the aging of some substances. For example, diethyl ether forms diethyl peroxide when exposed to sunlight, a process called peroxidation. Ether becomes dangerously unstable after peroxidation has occurred. Old containers of ether must be removed by qualified professionals and detonated at a site used to dispose of various explosives.

The primary commercial use of hydrogen peroxide is as a bleaching agent. Hydrogen peroxide is a powerful oxidizing agent, destroying organic compounds that come into contact with it. Hydrogen peroxide acts as a bleach by oxidizing and destroying pigments. Bleaching solutions normally have concentrations of 30 percent hydrogen peroxide. Much hydrogen peroxide is used to bleach cotton, wool, and ground wood pulp for paper, as well as in hair bleaching formulations. In the bleaching process, colored organic materials such as lignin and melanin are treated with hydrogen peroxide, destroying the color. Hydrogen peroxide is ideal for bleaching materials such as hair, silk, feathers, straw, teeth, gelatin, and flour because the process produces oxygen and water, neither of which is toxic or caustic.

Melanin is a pigment responsible for the color of black and brown hair. These colors are the result of pigment molecules composed of carbon atoms linked together with alternating single and double bonds. When hair is bleached using a

10 percent solution of hydrogen peroxide, the H_2O_2 molecules break the double bonds in the pigment molecules. Oxygen released by the hydrogen peroxide bonds with carbon atoms in the chain, forming three-membered rings called epoxides. The hair color disappears as the alternating sequence of single and double bonds is disrupted. The bleaching process can be damaging to hair, leaving it fragile and brittle.

Honey, which contains trace amounts of hydrogen peroxide, was once used as an antiseptic dressing for wounds. Commercially prepared hydrogen peroxide is sold to hospitals and to the public in 3 percent solutions as an antiseptic. Hydrogen peroxide is also used to supply oxygen to various fuel mixtures in rockets and torpedoes.

In the art world, hydrogen peroxide is used to restore old paintings by converting black lead sulfide in pigments to the original white color of lead sulfate.

Finally, hydrogen peroxide plays a role in air pollution. Hydrogen peroxide decomposes in the presence of light. Peroxide fragments such as HO_2 and HO react with unburned fuel molecules, converting them into substances called lacrymators. Lacrymators are chemical irritants that make the eyes water. The tear ducts respond to invasion by these chemicals by secreting a saline fluid in an attempt to wash the chemicals away. This hydrogen peroxide type of air pollution is a component of photochemical smog.

1. What is the chemical makeup of hydrogen peroxide?

_____

2. How does hydrogen peroxide bleach hair?

_____

_____

_____

3. What advantage does hydrogen peroxide have over other bleaching agents such as chlorine gas?

_____

_____

4. How does hydrogen peroxide contribute to photochemical smog?

_____

_____

5. Many hair coloring products are advertised as "self-timing," indicating that the bleaching process somehow shuts down after a period of time. Explain how this is possible.

_____

_____

6. In the reaction between melanin and hydrogen peroxide, which substance is oxidized? Which substance is reduced? Explain your answer.

_____

_____

Electroplating: A Coat of Many Ions

Metals have played an important part in the development of civilization. Humans have always been fascinated by the luster of metals such as gold, silver, and copper. These elements and their alloys have been used in jewelry, weapons, and coinage for centuries. Unfortunately, they have been a cause of conflict between peoples for almost as long.

Some metals, such as iron and copper, react with oxygen in the air and corrode. Other metals are so malleable, which means they are readily deformed, that using them in pure form often is not feasible. For example, a solid gold ring could never withstand the bangs and bumps of everyday life without becoming bent and dented. Coating a metal object with a thin layer of a second metal can protect the metal object from corrosion. It can also enhance the appearance of the object while providing durability and reducing expense or weight. The process of using an electric current to coat an object with a thin layer of metal is called electroplating. Electroplating is widely used to change the surface properties of various articles for consumer and industrial use. Jewelry, eating utensils, and other products are electroplated with gold and silver to improve their appearance. Such articles would be very expensive if they were made of solid silver or gold. To make them last longer, tools, bumpers on vehicles, cooking utensils, and similar articles are electroplated to resist corrosion. Circuit boards consist of thin metallic patterns electroplated onto a surface. You may have seen circuit boards in computers, calculators, and a multitude of other electronic devices.

The electroplating process is relatively simple. An electrolytic solution called a bath contains a salt of the metal used for plating. Most salts are electrolytes, which are substances that conduct electricity when in solution or in a molten state. Typically, ionic compounds, made up of a metal ion and a nonmetal ion or a polyatomic ion, are electrolytes. In such substances, positive and negative ions dissociate and will conduct current in solution. Copper(II) sulfate and silver nitrate are examples of salts used in electroplating procedures. The article to be plated—a spoon, ring, or pliers—is connected to a cathode in the bath. The cathode is the negative terminal of a voltage source, such as a battery. The other terminal, the anode, is connected to a piece of the same metal as that found in the salt or to a conductor that is not affected by the reaction. The article is plated to the appropriate thickness with the desired metal by passing a low-voltage current through the solution.

Figure 1   Electroplating Apparatus

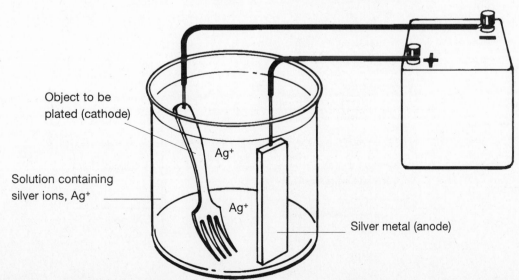

Object to be plated (cathode)

Solution containing silver ions, Ag$^+$

Ag$^+$

Ag$^+$

Silver metal (anode)

Metallic salt solutions are excellent conductors, so even low voltages produce good results. Because the voltage must be direct current for the article to be plated, DC, or direct-current, generators are used or a rectifier is employed to convert the voltage to DC.

As electroplating proceeds, the concentration of the salt in solution must be maintained by the addition of crystals of the plating salt or by replacing or replenishing the anode if it is made of the plating metal. A firm bond between the article and the deposited metal is produced when one metal tends to dissolve in the other. If this bond is not formed, some intermediate metal, which will bond well with the article and the plate metal, is first deposited. For example, iron forms a poor bond with silver. Silver plated onto iron peels and flakes off. To silverplate iron, a thin layer of copper is first deposited on the iron. The silver then is plated onto the copper.

The thickness of the plating, the amount of metal deposited on an article, depends on the current, the plating time, and the efficiency of the cathode. Many factors affect the plating reaction, including the voltage, the conductivity of the plating solution, and the distance between the terminals. A property called the throwing power identifies the degree to which the plating thickness is uniform. Obtaining a uniform thickness of plating on an irregularly-shaped object is difficult because not all parts of the object are equally distant from the anode. Magnetic gauges can be used to test plate thickness if either the plating material or the article itself is ferromagnetic, or attracted to a magnet. If the article is ferromagnetic, the force of attraction decreases as the thickness of the plating increases. If the plating metal is ferromagnetic, the force of attraction increases as the thickness increases. Other methods used to measure plate thickness include measuring backscattering of radiation striking the material, examining a cross section under a microscope, and using a chemical test that measures the amount of time necessary to dissolve the coating.

Preparation of the article to be plated is crucial. Metallic coatings will not adhere to a surface that is not scrupulously clean of oils, oxides, sulfides, and other contaminants. Grease is a primary contaminant, and several methods are used to remove this material. Most of these methods involve the use of an alkaline solution that reacts with the grease. Ultrasonic cleaning, in which high-frequency sound waves loosen contaminants, is used on dirty articles that have many crevices or small holes.

A process called pickling is used to prepare some metals, especially steel, for plating. A chemical bath is used to dissolve oxides on the surface of the base metal prior to electroplating. Steel is bathed in warm, dilute sulfuric acid because the acid is inexpensive and the reaction occurs rapidly at room temperature. Pickling greatly increases the adhesion of the plated material to the base metal.

Most large plating operations use conveyor

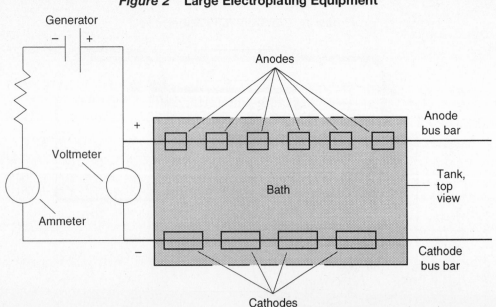

Figure 2 **Large Electroplating Equipment**

tanks in which articles move through a plating solution. This method, shown in Figure 2, improves the quality of the finished product and reduces the time needed to produce it. In semiautomatic conveyors, cathode racks move through a plating tank. Fully automatic conveyors move the cathodes through successive tanks containing cleaning, pickling, and plating solutions, with rinsing solutions in between.

Electroplating allows table utensils to be silver plated, jewelry to be plated in either silver or gold, and various components used outdoors to be weatherproofed by plating with cadmium or chromium. A highly polished finish may be given to an object by electroplating it with nickel. The ornamental chrome so popular on some automobile bumpers, side-view mirror mounts, and trim, as well as on household and business-office items such as pens and desk accessories, is produced by electroplating. These items usually are plated with copper and then with nickel before being plated with 0.025 to 0.127 millimeters of chromium. Chromium forms a bright, hard, corrosion-resistant, weatherproof surface. Hard chromium is plated onto rotating shafts in machinery because it is very wear resistant. A drawback of chromium-plated articles is that the plating often cracks and exposes the undercoat, which then will quickly corrode.

Copper is frequently used as an undercoat for electroplated articles, but it is also plated onto materials used for electrical and electronic applications. Printed circuit boards typically contain copper, which is thinly plated onto a sheet of plastic or laminate, completely covering the surface. The copper circuit is produced by masking those portions of the copper that form the circuit, then treating the surface with an acid solution that removes the rest of the plating. Gold is used in limited applications for circuits where the need for high conductivity and corrosion resistance overrides the cost of the element. Gold plating is also used in preparing lower-cost jewelry.

Electroplating is evident in many products, including plumbing pipes, jewelry, and corrosion-resistant building materials. Electroplating improves the ability of a material to withstand wear and tear and enhances the appearance of objects made with less appealing metals. It can even be used to make fine changes in the sizes of very small materials such as those used in electronics. As our dependence on electronic equipment grows and electroplating techniques become even finer, electroplating will become even more important to our economy.

1. What are some of the advantages of electroplating objects?

_____

_____

_____

_____

_____

2. Describe the process used to electroplate a material.

_____

_____

_____

_____

_____

3. Why would a ferromagnetic material be less attracted to a magnet as the thickness of a nonferromagnetic plating material increases?

_____

_____

_____

_____

4. How could electroplating be used to correct the dimensions of a metallic component that is a bit too small?

_____

_____

_____

_____

5. How does increasing the current applied to the solution affect the electroplating process?

_____

_____

_____

_____

Benzene: The Making of an Organic Chemical CHAPTER 18

he manufacture of the aromatic organic compound benzene is a leading example of technology's ability to be both a blessing and a curse. Benzene is an intermediate in the manufacture of many chemicals and materials that enable people to live more comfortably. However, the processes in which benzene is produced and used result in the formation of substances that can pollute the air, water, and land. Thus, by looking at the techniques, risks, benefits, and regulations involved in the manufacture of benzene, you can learn a little about the overall problem of producing chemicals.

Benzene, the structure of which is shown in Figure 1, is the simplest aromatic compound. It has a relatively low boiling point and high vapor pressure. So, under ordinary conditions it gives off vapors that have a strong, somewhat pleasant smell. Benzene was isolated in 1825 by Michael Faraday, who extracted it from the residue left after burning gas used at that time for home lighting. In 1845, A.W. Hofmann discovered that benzene could be extracted from coal tar, which is a by-product of the distillation of coal carried out to produce coke for steel-making. Soon thereafter, a small industry developed in which coal tar was distilled to yield light oil, benzene, and related aromatic compounds such as toluene and xylene.

Figure 1
Benzene

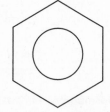

Before World War I, benzene's major industrial use was as a solvent in the rubber industry. During the war, there was an increased need for benzene as a precursor of toluene, which was used to make TNT and related explosives. As so often happens, the increased production of benzene and its derivatives led to a multiplication of its uses. Benzene's role as a solvent grew in such industries as the manufacture of rubber and artificial leather. Its role as an intermediate also expanded, as it became important in the manufacture of insecticides, detergents, dyes, adhesives, resins, drugs, flavorings, fragrances, and plastics.

As more uses were found for benzene and its products, steel-making was unable to provide sufficient coal tar for benzene production, and chemical companies looked elsewhere for a source. The young petroleum industry had been growing in the United States since the late 19th century, and research was progressing on the separation of the various components of crude oil. During the 1920s, methods were found not only to separate naturally occurring aromatics such as benzene from crude oil and natural gas, but also to convert other crude-oil components into aromatic compounds. Today, 98 percent of the benzene produced in the U.S. comes from the petrochemical and petroleum refining industries.

Benzene does occur naturally in crude oil and natural gas, but the amounts are quite small, usually 0.1–3.0 percent by volume. Thus, in order to meet the wide demand for aromatic chemicals, it is necessary to convert a portion of other petroleum components into benzene.

The first step in petroleum refining is distillation, in which differences in boiling points of the various crude-oil components are used to separate (fractionate) the components. In the distillation unit shown in Figure 2, all material boiling at 140°C and below (including benzene, which boils at 80.1°C) is removed at the top and redistilled for separation.

The fractions that boil at higher temperatures contain a variety of long-chain alkanes and alkenes, as well as some cyclic compounds with large numbers of carbon atoms. A method called catalytic cracking converts long hydrocarbon chains into smaller ones. The catalyst, often alumina and silica, is varied to increase the yield of specific hydrocarbons. Hydrocracking, in which hydrogen is added under pressure, is another method of cracking. In hydrocracking, the pressure and temperature can be varied to increase the yield of specific products. A catalyst, often platinum or palladium, is used to enable the reactions to take place at lower pressures and

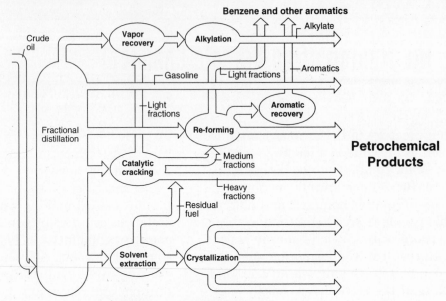

Figure 2   **Distillation Unit**

temperatures than otherwise would be required. Hydrocracking produces alkanes, whereas alkenes are the major products in the absence of added hydrogen.

The next step in the manufacture of benzene is catalytic re-forming, which converts smaller nonaromatic hydrocarbons into cyclic compounds. The removal of methyl groups and hydrogen converts these cyclic compounds to aromatic compounds. A typical series of catalytic re-forming reactions may be seen in Figure 3.

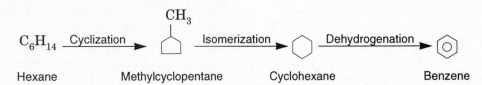

Figure 3   **Catalytic Re-forming Reactions**

As noted above, benzene is an intermediate in the making of many other organic chemicals. Several of these are shown in Figure 4.

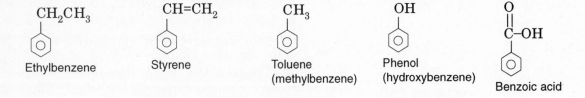

Figure 4   **Organic Chemicals Produced Using Benzene**

When benzene reacts with ethylene, ethyl benzene results; this compound is then dehydrogenated to form styrene, one of the most important petrochemical products. Styrene is polymerized to form polystyrene, a versatile plastic used in foams, resins, and synthetic rubber. Polystyrene plastic is found in packaging, household goods, toys, and appliances. Polyurethane, used in furniture cushions, and polyester in fabric blends that are used to make garments are also made from benzene. Toluene, or methylbenzene, has been important in its own right as a solvent, although this use is decreasing because toluene is toxic. However, toluene is still important as an intermediate in the manufacture of explosives, benzoic acid, and phenol. Benzoic acid

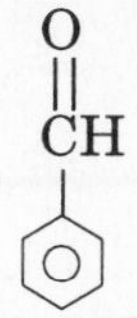

O
‖
CH

Benzaldehyde
(found in bitter almonds)

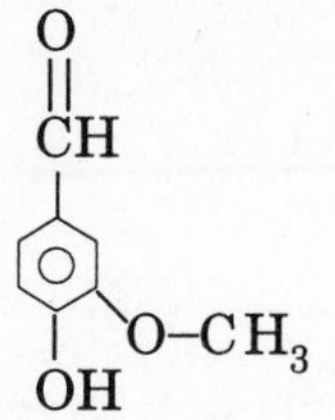

O
‖
CH

O–CH$_3$
OH

Vanillin
(found in vanilla bean)

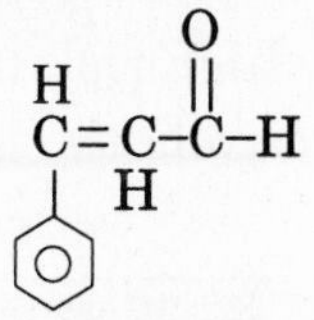

H   O
‖   ‖
C=C–C–H
H

Cinnamaldehyde
(found in cinnamon)

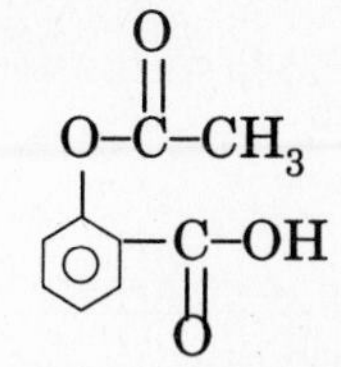

O
‖
O–C–CH$_3$

C–OH
‖
O

Acetylsalicylic acid
(aspirin)

Figure 5 Some Common Flavorings and Drugs

and phenol are important in drug manufacture and in the preparation of many flavorings and fragrances as well as other compounds. Figure 5 shows the structures of a few of these products.

The annual U.S. production of benzene is several million tons. Benzene has vast economic importance and reaches into every area of modern life and industry. However, in recent years, benzene has also been shown to be harmful to living organisms, including humans. The risks of benzene production begin at the oil well, where spills or fires can contaminate the ground or air. In addition, petroleum refining produces sulfur dioxide, SO_2, which results from the sulfur often found in crude oil. The sulfur dioxide contributes to such problems as acid rain. However, companies can also collect and sell the sulfur in the oil as a by-product. The refining process also produces toxic sludges, which present a disposal problem. Benzene itself can spill, leak, and burn. During the 1980s, it was estimated that about 300 000 tons per year leaked into the environment. The Environmental Protection Agency (EPA) classifies benzene as both an ignitable and a toxic waste; toluene also falls into this category.

Benzene also requires great care in manufac-

turing, handling, and use because it is a carcinogen that can cause leukemia and other cancers of the blood. The first report that benzene could affect the bone marrow was published in 1897. Residues and vapors from many processes that begin with benzene as an intermediate may be toxic, flammable, and even explosive under some conditions.

Much has been done to make the petrochemical industry provide safeguards. Measures include use of closed systems, vapor recovery equipment to capture escaping fumes, recycling and conversion of solvents into less toxic materials, and close regulation of disposal in well-protected landfills or by incineration.

Without benzene and its products, the world's economy would be much poorer. Synthetic rubber and many fabrics and plastics would be nonexistent; the printing industry would be less advanced. Much of the variety of products that we take for granted would be gone. At the same time, the manufacture and use of this versatile, important chemical can cause risks to health. One of the primary challenges to the chemical industry today is finding ways to produce and use such chemicals in safer ways.

1. How is benzene manufactured from crude oil?

_____

_____

_____

_____

_____

_____

2. Groups that encounter high risk from benzene toxicity include refinery workers. Name at least three other groups that might be at risk.

   _____

   _____

   _____

3. Which alkanes would you expect to distill from the fractionating tower in the
   fraction containing benzene?

   _____

   _____

4. Typical cracking reactions are: $C_{10}H_{22} + H_2 \rightarrow C_6H_{14} + C_4H_{10}$, and $C_9H_{20} \rightarrow$
   $C_5H_{10} + C_4H_{10}$. Which of these is an example of hydrocracking? How do the
   products of hydrocracking and ordinary high-temperature cracking differ? Why
   do they differ?

   _____

   _____

   _____

   _____

   _____

   _____

5. What are some industrial chemicals for which benzene is an intermediate?

   _____

   _____

6. World War I increased demand for benzene and prompted the development of
   new uses. Why do you think that increased production of a chemical leads to
   the discovery of new uses?

   _____

   _____

   _____

   _____

   _____

Name _____

Date _____ Class _____

Flavors and Fragrances: Waking Up Your Senses

ou probably think about your senses of smell and taste much less often than you think about the other senses, but these two related senses contribute a great deal to life. Smell and taste are chemical senses stimulated by the contact of molecules with nerve endings in the nose and mouth. The perception of taste and smell by the brain has many effects on behavior. The flavor of food is important to its appeal, and many eating choices are based on taste. Ancient peoples were aware of the effects of odors and utilized them. Incense, for example, has long been an important part of religious ceremonies among the ancient Hebrews, Egyptians, and Greeks. It is probable that even prehistoric people sought to find flavors and scents with which to enhance their food and their surroundings.

In earlier times, of course, the only fragrances and flavors were those that were found in nature. It is still the case today that most such substances are derived from natural sources. Most incense ingredients still come from the resins or gums of trees and other plants; many of the most expensive perfume ingredients are from pressed flower petals; most herbs, spices, and flavorings used in cooking are from plants.

People have long attempted to isolate the flavorful and fragrant substances found in plants. As early as the eleventh century, gentle heating of plant material followed by distillation was employed to recover such compounds. Variations of this method are still used on plant materials to obtain their "essential oils," so called because they were thought to contain the "essence" of the plant. An essential oil is rarely a single, pure chemical; it may be made up of dozens or even hundreds of different components. In many cases, trace materials are necessary to the scent and/or flavor of the oil. Such oils tend to have strong aromas and flavors and may be used in perfumes, incense, and cooking.

The essential oils in a perfume are dissolved in a solvent, usually alcohol, which generally evaporates as soon as the perfume is applied. The complex mixture of oils then slowly evaporates into the air, aided by the heat of the body. The perceived scent depends upon the number of molecules of each ingredient that reach the nose. It has been estimated that as few as eight molecules hitting an olfactory cell, a smell receptor within the nose, can produce a nerve impulse. These impulses are conducted to the brain where, in a complex and poorly understood interaction, they produce a mental and even an emotional response. One part of the brain that is affected is that involved with memory. Scientists have verified the fact that suddenly experiencing a fragrance or flavor can elicit vivid remembrances.

Many kinds of compounds are found in perfumes and flavorings. These include compounds classed as aldehydes, aromatics, terpenes, steroids, alcohols, esters, and acids. They are all organic chemicals—compounds of carbon.

Many fruity odors and flavors are esters. In an ester, an oxygen atom is bonded to two different carbon atoms. A second oxygen atom is double-bonded to one of the two carbon atoms. The aromas of bananas, pineapples, pears, apples, grapes, oranges, and many other fruits are due mostly to esters.

Other flavors and fragrances are due to aldehydes, which are organic chemicals that contain oxygen double-bonded to a carbon. An example of an aromatic aldehyde is vanillin, which is isolated from the vanilla bean. Vanillin is used extensively as a flavoring in candies and baked goods. Cinnamaldehyde, from cinnamon, and benzaldehyde, from bitter almonds, are other aromatic aldehydes.

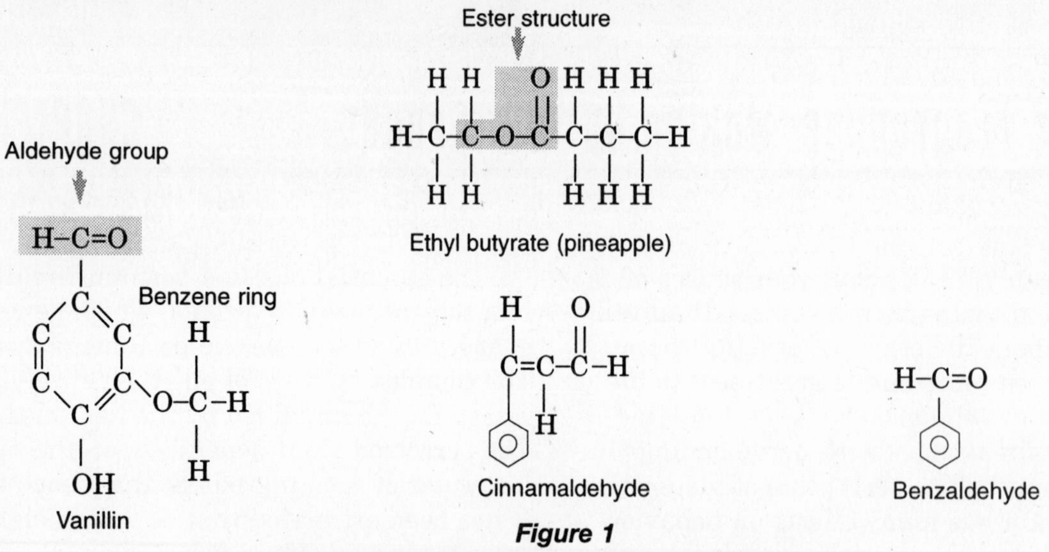

Ester structure

H H   O H H H
| | || | | |
H–C–C–O–C–C–C–C–H
| | | | |
H H   H H H

Ethyl butyrate (pineapple)

Aldehyde group

H–C=O

Vanillin

Benzene ring

H

O–C–H

OH

H

Cinnamaldehyde

H   O
\ ||
C=C–C–H
|
H

Benzaldehyde

H–C=O

Figure 1
Some Compounds in Perfumes and Flavorings

The most important components of essential oils are terpenes, organic chemicals that have the general formula $C_{10}H_{16}$ and that have several double bonds. Important terpenes and their derivatives include geraniol, found in rose oil; limonene, from oil of lemon; citral, from lemongrass; and zingiberene, from oil of ginger.

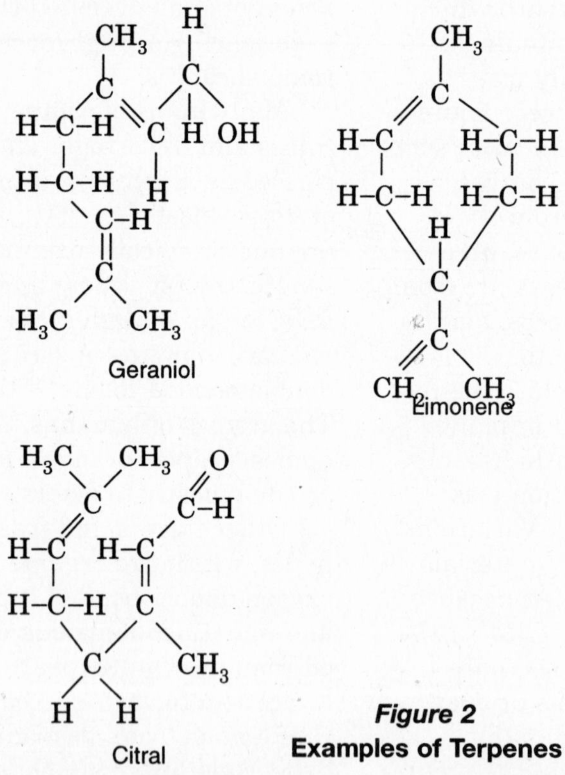

Geraniol

Limonene

Citral

Figure 2
Examples of Terpenes

Although many substances that produce flavors and fragrances can now be synthesized, the isolation of essential oils and other essences from plants is still vitally important. In the case of herbs and spices, the leaves, stems, flowers, or roots are used fresh or dried. Many fruit flavors are isolated from rind or juice.

In many cases, the processing of essential oils is complex and depends on such important physical characteristics as vapor pressure and solubility. Preparation of a typical essential oil, such as citral, involves cutting, grinding, or crushing the leaves and other plant parts, which liberates some of the oil. This process is followed by steam distillation, which is utilized to make the oil volatile. The oil vaporizes in the steam and is carried with it to a cooling container or condenser. As condensation of the steam occurs, the oil floats on top of the water and is collected. Distillation plants vary according to the type of oil being separated. Figure 3 shows a typical plant used to obtain oil from herbs, oil of peppermint, for example. Usually the entire essential oil, a mixture, is collected and used. However, methods of fractional distillation are making it possible to separate some of the individual components in the oil.

Another method of extracting essential oils,

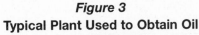

Typical Plant Used to Obtain Oil

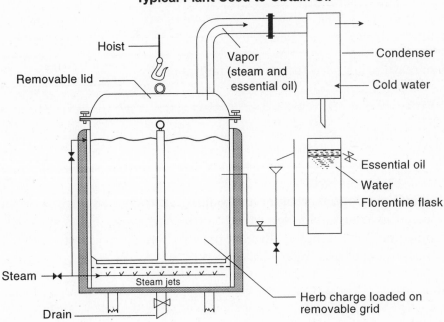

used particularly in cases where the flavor or scent component is heat-sensitive, is by pressing the oils out of the raw material and extracting the oils with fat or a hydrocarbon solvent. Pressing is often used with citrus oils and some delicate flowers.

Extraction of essential oils with fat is called enfleurage; it is used with some of the most delicate flower petals, such as jasmine. The essential oils resulting from this process are very expensive because the flower petals are spread on the fat by hand and changed periodically until the fat has absorbed as much of the odor-producing substances as possible. Then the oil is separated from the fat by extraction with alcohol.

The first synthesis of a natural scent was in 1868 when coumarin, which has the odor of freshly mown grass, was made in England. Synthetic fragrances and flavorings include both duplications of products found in nature, such as cinnamaldehyde, and new compounds, often patterned after, but differing from, known aromatics or terpenes. Because of the great complexity of natural essential oils, duplication is not an easy task. Imitation strawberry flavor, for example, may contain twelve or more organic substances, including several aldehydes and esters.

After isolation or synthesis, fragrances and flavorings are packaged. As might be expected, flavorings are under strict government control. In fact, to qualify as "natural," flavorings must have been isolated exclusively by physical means and not have been subjected to any chemical change.

The flavor and fragrance industries play an important role in the world's economy. The cosmetics industry sells a vast amount of perfumes and colognes every year. There are more than 800 brands of perfume alone. Scents are used in almost all soaps, deodorants, shampoos, powders, and make-up. Scents are also used in detergents, fabric softeners, and room fresheners. Even some packaging and stationery is scented.

Nearly every package of prepared food lists among the ingredients "natural and artificial flavors," and flavors are the largest single group of intentional food additives. Many companies in the flavoring and fragrance business spend a significant proportion of their research and development funds on the isolation or synthesis of aromas or flavors and on testing consumer responses to them. One need only watch television for a short time to appreciate the amount of advertising creativity devoted to fragrances.

1. Probably about 40 olfactory cells must be stimulated before a smell sensation is detected. Based on this fact, what is the minimum number of molecules needed to elicit a sense of odor?

    _____ ____

    _____

2. How is steam distillation used to extract essential oils?

    _____

    _____

    _____

3. According to legal regulations, cooking and baking extracts and flavorings that use only natural flavoring agents are called "pure"; those employing synthetics are called "imitation" or "artificial." From a purely chemical point of view, what is wrong with this sort of naming?

    _____

    _____

    _____

    _____

    _____

4. Name some possible factors to consider in choosing a solvent for extraction of essential oils. Would there be factors that should be considered with flavorings but not necessarily with fragrances?

    _____

    _____

    _____

    _____

    _____

    _____

Nylon: A Thousand and One Uses

The prefix *mono-* means "one." The prefix *poly-* means "many." Monomers are relatively small, individual molecules. Polymers are large molecules that are formed by linking many simpler monomers together with chemical bonds. Polymer chemistry is a relatively new field but plays a vital role in your life and in the economy.

Natural polymer fibers such as silk and cotton have been known for thousands of years. Cotton is a cellulose polymer; silk is a protein fiber. Aware of the qualities of these fibers, chemists investigated ways to prepare polymers in the laboratory. In 1884, the French chemist Chardonnet was successful in making a highly reflective material he called artificial silk by treating wood cellulose with nitric acid. The material was later given the name *rayon*. This forerunner of synthetic fibers has been greatly modified to improve its qualities since that time, but the discovery set the stage for polymer chemistry.

In 1928, an American, Wallace Carothers, went to work at DuPont, where he began polymer research with the goal of producing synthetic materials that had properties similar to those of silk. He studied a reaction between the monomers adipic acid and hexamethylenediamine. Adipic acid contains six carbon atoms with a carboxylic acid group, –COOH, on each of the end carbon atoms. Hexamethylenediamine contains six carbon atoms with an amino group, –NH$_2$, at each end. The reaction produced a long-chain polymer made up of six-carbon monomers linked by amide bonds between the carboxylic acid and amino groups. Carothers had made the

first completely synthetic fiber; it was given the name *Nylon 66*. The sixes refer to the number of carbon atoms in the two monomer units. Nylon 66 is the predominant form of nylon produced in the United States. Another polymer, Nylon 6, is commonly used in Europe. Nylon 6 uses a single type of monomer with an amino group at one end and a carboxylic acid group at the other end. Nylon 6 has slightly different properties from those of Nylon 66 and is made from a compound called caprolactam.

Initially, DuPont did not file a patent on nylon because it did not appear to have any useful properties. Another researcher, Julian Hill, noted that a ball of nylon on the end of a glass rod could be drawn out into a fiber that had a silky appearance. One day, Hill and his fellow workers tried to see how far they could stretch a sample. They ran down the hall with the ball of nylon on the rod, stretching it into a very long thread. The researchers realized that they were putting the molecules into a parallel orientation. This process increased the strength and the elasticity of the product. In 1940, the first nylon stockings were offered for sale in New York City and proved enormously popular. Shortly thereafter, nylons were removed from the market because nylon was needed for making parachutes in World War II.

Nylon is synthesized by a reaction called condensation polymerization. In this type of reaction, many hundreds of monomers react together to form long chains, eliminating a water molecule as each link in the chain is added. Molecules containing reactive groups at both ends are com-

Figure 1
Production of Nylon 66

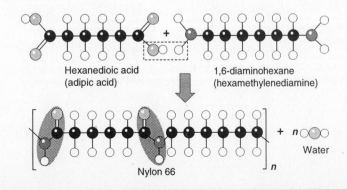

Hexanedioic acid (adipic acid)

1,6-diaminohexane (hexamethylenediamine)

Nylon 66

+ n Water

Figure 2
Part of Nylon Polymer Molecule

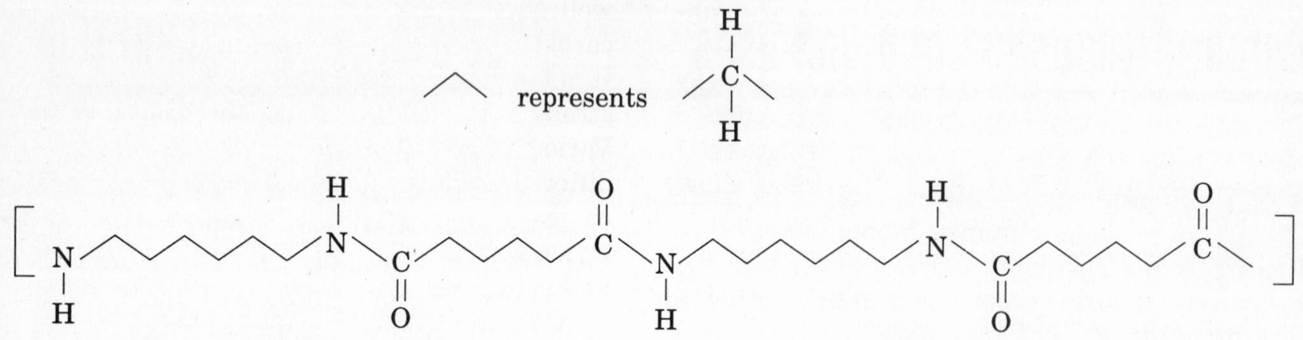

bined to yield larger molecules that also have reactive groups at both ends.

Nylon is a thermoplastic material, which means it can be softened by heating and solidified by cooling without altering its chemical nature. Nylon fibers are produced commercially by a process called extrusion. Nylon chips or pellets are fed into a melter, where the chips are heated until they melt. The melted nylon is then filtered and extruded through a spinneret. The spinneret is like a mechanical spider spinning strands for a web. Hot, molten polymer is extruded into a stream of cold air where it solidifies into filaments that can be as thin as a human hair. The solidified filaments are drawn or stretched out onto a drum, where they are cured for several days. Drawing or stretching increases the order of the nylon by extending the molecules of the filaments so that they pack more closely

together. It also orients the molecules along a single axis. The greater the orientation of the molecules, the greater will be the strength and elasticity. The spinning orients the molecules so that hydrogen bonds are formed between adjacent molecules. These bonds give nylon its great strength. Hydrogen bonds pull the fibers back to their original arrangement when the applied stress is removed. (Nylon stockings hug moving legs by virtue of the hydrogen bonds between their molecules.) After the curing period, the fiber is drawn again to increase its strength and elasticity. The yarn is wound onto a tube. This long, single fiber is called the staple. Nylon 66 can also be extruded from the reaction chamber and cut in the shape of cubes as well as being made into fibers. The cubes are used in molding processes.

Finally, the nylon is textured. Early nylon had distinct problems: the smooth, straight-

Figure 3
Nylon Polymer Molecule After Being Cold Drawn

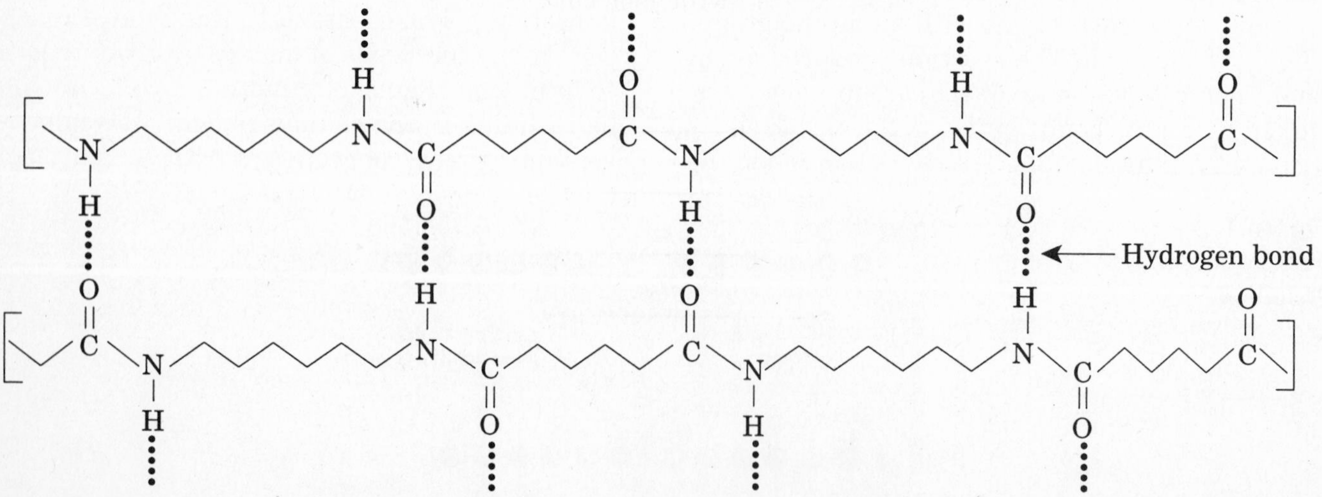

filament yarns produced poor moisture transport and poor insulation. The result was that the fabric felt cold and clammy. The fabric did not "breathe," or carry moisture such as sweat, away from the body. Minor alterations in the properties of nylon correct these problems. Texturing produces irregularities along the fiber that allow the fabric to transport moisture and make it a better insulator. After the nylon fiber has been woven into a fabric, it is heat set. Heat setting relaxes the fibers and provides permanent stability—no shrinking or wrinkling.

Nylon can be textured to resemble silk, linen, wool, and other natural fibers but has the advantages of being wear-resistant, wrinkle-free, and impervious to biological action by bacteria, fungi,

and insects. Nylon fibers also take and hold dyes well. The majority of nylon is manufactured for carpet, apparel, tire cords, and molded plastics. It is blended with other fibers to give it tensile strength and make it more abrasion resistant. Various types of nylons are on the market, and different nylons are useful in making such items as gears, bearings, brushes, and machine parts. Nylon wears well, can be molded into any shape, and is inexpensive to produce.

One unusual application of nylon is Velcro. Velcro is a two-part fastener made of nylon. One half is a surface covered with nylon loops; the other surface is covered with tiny hooks. When the surfaces are in contact, the hooks catch in the loops and make a good fastener.

1. Why is nylon considered a polymer?

_____

_____

_____

_____

2. Describe the chemical reaction used to produce Nylon 66.

_____

_____

_____

_____

3. How does drawing or stretching affect the molecules that make up nylon?

_____

_____

_____

_____

_____

4. What properties are improved by drawing nylon?

_____

_____

_____

_____

_____

5. What characteristics make nylon a better material for carpeting than natural fibers such as cotton or wool?

_____

_____

_____

_____

6. What properties make nylon a good material for parachutes?

_____

_____

_____

_____

_____

Dynamite: Manufacturing an Explosive Combination   CHAPTER 20

The best-known industrial explosive is dynamite, invented in 1867 by the Swedish chemist Alfred Nobel, who endowed the Nobel Prizes. He derived the name *dynamite* from the Greek word *dynamis,* meaning power. Dynamite contains nitroglycerin, a powerful but unstable chemical explosive, discovered by an Italian chemist, Ascanio Sobrero, in 1846. Nobel found that mixing nitroglycerin with kieselguhr, a porous, inert, chalky material, resulted in an explosive that was easier to use and safer to handle. Soon it was found that substituting oxidizers for a proportion of the kieselguhr improved the strength of the explosive without decreasing its stability.

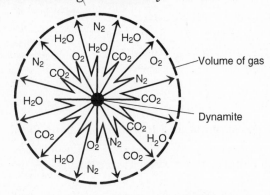

Figure 1   Detonation of Nitroglycerin

An explosive is a substance that reacts rapidly, producing a sudden, large burst of heat and gas. The chemical reaction in the detonation of nitroglycerin produces gaseous carbon dioxide, nitrogen, oxygen, and water vapor, as shown in Figure 1. The tremendous heat causes rapid expansion of these gases and also of the surrounding air. As the rapid oxidation of the explosive takes place, a high-pressure shock wave passes through the material at high speed, accelerating the exothermic decomposition of the chemicals. The heat and high-pressure shock wave have a shattering effect, which can be useful when controlled. The reaction is $4C_3H_5(ONO_2)_3(l) \rightarrow 12CO_2(g) + 10H_2O(g) + 6N_2(g) + O_2(g) + energy$.

In a typical explosion, 3700-4800 joules of heat per gram are liberated, and the pressure can reach 7 000 000 kPa. The temperature reaches several thousand degrees Celsius. A typical yield of gas is about 1000 mL per gram of explosive mixture. The very intense shock wave travels at a velocity of over a thousand meters per second. However, by varying the composition of the dynamite, the amount of gas produced, the amount of heat liberated, the pressure exerted on the surroundings, and the resulting shattering power can be adjusted.

Research on dynamite has continued, and now a wide variety of dynamites, manufactured for specific purposes, are available. Straight dynamite consists of nitroglycerin, $C_3H_5(ONO_2)_3$, with sodium nitrate, $(NaNO_3)$, as the main oxidizer. The power is determined by the percentage of nitroglycerin. Ethylene glycol dinitrate is usually added to the mixture to lower the freezing point and thus allow the dynamite to be used in cold places. Ammonia dynamites use ammonium nitrate, (NH_4NO_3), as part of the oxidizing mixture. They are used in hard-rock, underwater blasting. Low-density ammonia dynamites use a maximum of ammonium nitrate, resulting in dynamites that are cheaper and more stable than straight dynamite. Straight-gelatin dynamites use nitroglycerin that has been gelatinized with 2-8 percent nitrocellulose, resulting in explosives that are less sensitive than straight dynamites but that have greater shattering action. These dynamites also have improved resistance to water. The addition of about 10 percent sodium chloride to dynamite lowers the flame temperature of the decomposition products. This modification produces a dynamite that is safer for use in underground coal mines, where the air is likely to contain methane and flammable coal dust.

Due to its stability, dynamite requires a detonator, which is a flammable initiating agent and a high explosive. Formerly, detonators were made with mercury fulminate. Now, lead azide and silver azide are often used commercially, although military uses require more complex devices.

Obviously, manufacturing of any explosive is a hazardous process. Allowing a batch of dynamite to accumulate in a large vat would be dangerous indeed. Thus, a continuous process has been developed, as shown in Figure 2, so that the product is packaged as it is finished. Glycerol is nitrated with nitric acid under continuous cooling. The water produced in the reaction is absorbed by sulfuric acid. As it is made, the nitroglycerin is conducted through tubes into a mixer where it is combined with other fuels, oxidizers, sensitizers, waterproofing compounds, antifreezes, and stabilizers. Wastes are continuously conducted away, and the completed explosive passes through more pipes into cartridges lined with cylindrical paper. As the mixture is added to the cartridges in small quantities, a plunger compresses it. When the cylinder is full, the completed sticks of dynamite are packaged. Most sticks of dynamite are 2-20 cm in diameter and 20-91 cm in length.

Dynamite has been important in the building and settling of the United States and other nations. One of the first uses of dynamite in the United States was for blasting oil wells. It has been used in tunnel construction, in cutting passes through mountains, in coal mining, and in many types of construction. It is useful whenever large amounts of solid material must be broken up quickly. Using any explosive is extremely dangerous, and special training is necessary for anyone handling it. The uses of explosives have

grown, but the use of dynamite has declined as new types of explosives, including TNA and plastic explosives, have been developed.

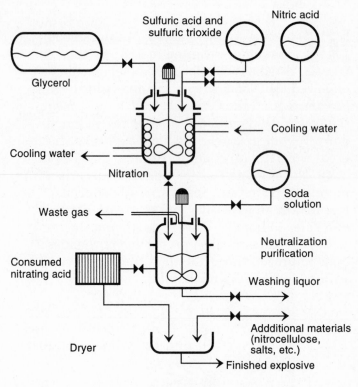

Figure 2
Continuous-Process Explosives Plant

1. Describe what is happening chemically in the detonation of a typical explosive such as dynamite.

   _____

   _____

2. Why are different types of dynamite manufactured?

   _____

   _____

3. Describe how dynamite is manufactured.

   _____

   _____

   _____

4. How does the pressure exerted by the gases produced in an explosion change as the gases expand rapidly after the explosion?

   _____

1 • Paper: Just What Really Goes into Each Piece?

1. Before the nineteenth century, paper was made out of limited quantities of rag fibers rather than from wood, and it was made by hand.

2. The fibers are held together by tiny hooklike fibrils, which are exposed during the beating process.

3. NaOH is sodium hydroxide; Na_2S is sodium sulfide; and Na_2SO_4 is sodium sulfate.

4. Sodium hydroxide is part of the original *white liquor* that reduces the wood chips to pulp. During this process it is converted to sodium carbonate, which is part of the *black liquor* that is washed out of the pulp. This sodium carbonate is filtered and treated with lime, converting it back to sodium hydroxide, which, in turn, is used in a new batch of white liquor.

5. Mechanical pulping, compared with the other processes, results in a greater yield of pulp from the amount of wood used. However, the cellulose fibers are so badly damaged by the grinding that the paper produced is quite weak.

6. To make each sheet of the first paper, a screen was dipped into a mixture of cellulose fibers in water and each sheet had to dry. Modern machinery produces paper continuously, producing many more sheets in much less time.

4 • Oxygen: More Than Thin Air

1. It was a by-product of processes of certain early organisms and probably poisoned living things not adapted to it.

2. The ozone acts as a filter to absorb some of the ultraviolet radiation that falls on our planet from the sun. The UV breaks down oxygen molecules, freeing oxygen atoms, which then react with molecular oxygen to produce ozone. This process keeps some of the UV from getting through. UV is also absorbed by the ozone molecules.

3. Air is liquefied using high pressures and low temperatures, then the components are separated by applying heat to vaporize each one. Each component boils at a different temperature so each can be drawn off at a specific temperature.

4. The oxygen reacts chemically with the carbon and other elements to form substances that can be removed.

5. The hot water would warm the streams or lakes, reducing the amount of oxygen in them and threatening organisms that depend on the oxygen.

5 • Sulfur: Using Earth's Yellow Mineral

1. It yields sulfur that is 99.5 percent pure, and it does not involve the use of toxic substances.

2. Mosquitoes don't like the taste or smell of blood that contains high concentrations of sulfur compounds. Also, sulfa drugs fight infections that might develop.

3. Millions of tons are involved annually, and 5 percent of this quantity is still a great deal of sulfur dioxide to permit to enter the atmosphere.

4. Partial burning of the hydrogen sulfide produces an atmosphere containing both unreacted hydrogen sulfide and some product sulfur dioxide. Both substances must be available for the reaction that then yields elemental sulfur.

5. Hydrogen sulfide has a very obvious odor. The addition of it allows an odorless gas, such as propane or methane, to be detected in the event of a leak before an explosion occurs.

6. The addition of sulfur changes the physical properties of natural rubber so that the substance is more useful.

7. High-sulfur petroleum produces large quantities of pollutants such as sulfur dioxide, which is not acceptable. Desulfurization techniques must be developed to make these petroleum resources viable.

6 • The Making of Ammonia

1. The two main factors were the need to produce nitrogen fertilizers and the need to use ammonia to manufacture explosives.

2. Nitrogen and hydrogen are combined directly at high pressures and temperatures in the presence of a catalyst.

3. Large-scale food production requires large plots of land that yield maximum crop production for the acreage. Ammonia is used to produce fertilizers that greatly enhance crop yield.

4. It is used for so many products and processes.

5. Aquatic plant growth increases in the presence of fertilizer leading to oxygen depletion and the possible death of a body of water.

6. Because the reaction is reversible, a point would be reached at which ammonia is converted back to nitrogen and hydrogen as fast as it is produced. Removing ammonia prevents this condition of equilibrium from being reached.

7 • Synthetic Gems: The Making of All That Glitters

1. It means that it is rigid and that the particles in it are arranged in a repeating pattern, resulting in a certain geometric shape.

2. Characteristics include hardness, or resistance to being scratched, and toughness, or resistance to fracture and cleavage.

3. Both are varieties of the mineral corundum (Al_2O_3). Rubies are red and contain traces of chromium. Sapphires maybe any other color.

4. Very pure corundum and chromium(III) oxide are fused.

5. The hydrothermal process is the most common.

6. They are used as long-lasting bearings in watches, meters, and other small mechanical devices.

7. Diamond is a network crystal. The covalent bonding is strong and extends in three dimensions, making it difficult for atoms to be scratched away or to leave the crystal and enter the liquid state.

8 • Glass: Is It Really Only Melted Sand?

1.

$$
\begin{array}{c}
:\!\overset{\cdot\cdot}{O}: \\
\overset{\cdot\cdot}{}\;\;\overset{\cdot\times}{}\;\;\overset{\cdot\cdot}{} \\
:\!O \!\times\! Si \!\times\! O: \\
\overset{\cdot\cdot}{}\;\;\overset{\cdot\times}{}\;\;\overset{\cdot\cdot}{} \\
:\!\overset{\cdot\cdot}{O}:
\end{array}
$$

2. Most materials that might be used for the ovens will dissolve in molten silica.

3. If molten silica is cooled rapidly, crystals do not have a chance to form, and the silica maintains the arrangement of a liquid.

4. Vitreous glass (fused silica) would be most useful.

5. Possible answers include: the automobile industry: windshields, headlights, spark-plug bodies; home-construction industry: windows, fiberglass insulation, solar panels, electric insulators, ornaments; the lighting industry: lamps, light bulbs; the food industry: cooking/baking vessels, jars, bottles.

6. Answers may include lead exposure, burns, and heat exhaustion. Some students may also refer to silicosis, a lung disease resulting from inhalation of silica dust.

9 • Hydrogen: More Than Just the "H" in H₂O

1. Hydrogen is an invisible gas that burns in air, combining with oxygen.

2. A hydrogen atom has a single proton in the nucleus and a single electron in the first energy level. Isotopes of hydrogen containing one and two neutrons also occur. On Earth, hydrogen consists of molecules, each made up of two hydrogen atoms joined by a covalent bond.

3. In the laboratory, hydrogen is prepared by the reaction of an acid with a metal or by the passage of an electric current through water. Commercially, hydrogen is produced by the reaction of steam with white-hot carbon or hydrocarbons.

4. Hydrogen is used in the production of ammonia and in the production of hydrochloric acid. Hydrogen is used in the production of methanol and in the extraction of certain metals, such as tungsten, from their oxides.

5. Liquid hydrogen is used in cryogenics and superconductivity studies, in fuel cells, and in rocket cells.

13 • Soaps and Detergents: a Very "Clean" Industry

1. Soaps have a nonpolar end that embeds in oils or fats and a polar end that is attracted to water molecules. Thus, soap molecules pick up oils and fats so that they can be rinsed away.

2. A soap is a salt of a fatty acid. An alkali metal ion, such as potassium, is associated with the fatty acid ion.

3. Fat is made to react with alkali, such as potassium hydroxide, often in a large kettle. Soap and glycerol are produced. The glycerol is rinsed away.

4. Soap reacts with the magnesium and calcium ions in hard water to produce lime soap, or scum. This substance is not water-soluble and deposits on the laundry, washer drum, and sink.

14 • Sulfuric Acid: The Mark of a Healthy Economy

1. Sulfuric acid is the most massively produced chemical in the world, and it is used in a tremendous number of industries. When these industries are healthy—that is, producing and selling many goods—the production of sulfuric acid is high.

2. phosphate fertilizers

3. lead-chamber process

4. The waste gases are potent air pollutants that normally are vented into the atmosphere. When used to produce sulfuric acid, these gases are recycled inside the plant.

5. In the contact process, vanadium pentoxide catalyzes the reaction of sulfur dioxide to sulfur trioxide, which would otherwise proceed very slowly.

6. sulfurous acid, because it contains less oxygen than does H_2SO_4

7. acidic anhydrides, because adding water to the oxides would turn them into their corresponding acids

8. H_2SO_4 is much more ionized in water solution.

9. Cogeneration is the use of normally wasted heat energy produced in an industrial process to generate electricity. All the reactions in the production of sulfic acid are exothermic. Hence, a sulfuric acid plant produces an enormous amount of heat energy. This energy is used to change water to steam that powers turbines which turn electric generators to produce electricity.

16 • Hydrogen Peroxide: Not Just a Hairdresser's Tool

1. Hydrogen peroxide is composed of two hydrogen atoms and two oxygen atoms.

2. Hydrogen peroxide breaks the double bonds in the melanin, or pigment molecules. This change causes the color to be destroyed.

3. Hydrogen peroxide decomposes into water and

oxygen, which are not toxic.

4. Fragments of peroxide react with unburned fuel molecules, forming eye irritants called lacrymators. These substances are part of photochemical smog.

5. The reaction between melanin in the hair and hydrogen peroxide is a chemical reaction. When the hydrogen peroxide has been used up or no more melanin is available, the reaction is complete.

6. Melanin is oxidized, giving up electrons to oxygen released by the hydrogen peroxide. Hydrogen peroxide is reduced when it releases an oxygen atom that gains electrons.

17 • Electroplating: A Coat of Many Ions

1. Electroplating protects some metals from corrosion by covering them with corrosion-resistant metal. Electroplating also allows expensive, lustrous, but perhaps less durable metals to be used as a coating over less appealing metals that are less expensive and more resistant to damage.

2. An electrolytic bath containing a salt of the metal used for plating is prepared. The object to be plated is attached to the negative side, or cathode, of the electrical source. The positive side, or anode, is attached to a piece of metal of the type used in plating or to another material not affected by the reaction. A voltage applied to the system causes electrons to flow, and the metal in solution plates out on the cathode.

3. As the plating thickness increases, the distance between the magnet or gauge and the ferromagnetic substrate increases. The greater the distance, the smaller the magnetic force.

4. Application of a thicker coating would increase the size of the component.

5. Increasing the current would increase the rate at which electroplating occurred.

18.1 • Benzene: The Making of an Organic Chemical

1. Distillation of crude oil separates benzene into fractions based on differences in boiling point. Catalytic re-forming is used to convert hydrocarbons

Copyright © Glencoe/McGraw-Hill, a division of The McGraw-Hill Companies, Inc.

from some of the fractions into cyclic hydrocarbons. These compounds are converted to benzene and other aromatics by the removal of methyl groups and hydrogens.

2. Other groups include workers in the tire industry and other rubber workers, shoemakers who work with artificial leather, chemical workers, laboratory workers, and workers who transport benzene.

3. Students should list alkanes that boil at 140°C or lower. These are the lighter alkanes (octane, heptane, hexane, pentane, butane, propane, ethane, and methane).

4. The reaction $C_{10}H_{22} + H_2 \rightarrow C_6H_{14} + C_4H_{10}$ is hydrocracking. Hydrocracking yields alkanes, whereas ordinary cracking produces some alkenes, such as C_5H_{10} in the example. In ordinary cracking, there are not enough hydrogen atoms to form only alkanes as the chains are split, so some unsaturated hydrocarbons will result. Addition of hydrogen to the cracking mixture solves this problem.

5. Such chemicals include ethylbenzene, polystyrene, polyurethane, polyester, and toluene.

6. With increased production, the supply of a chemical becomes abundant and its price drops. Thus, it is to the advantage of industries to look for new ways to use the compound and for new products that can be made from it.

18.2 • Flavors and Fragrances: Waking up Your Senses

1. At 8 molecules per olfactory cell, 40 cells require 320 molecules for an odor to be detected.

2. Essential oil that has been obtained by grinding and crushing plant parts is vaporized with steam. The vapor is carried to a cooling container. After condensation, the oil floats on the water and is collected.

3. Although an essential oil is "natural" or "purely natural," it is composed of many different substances, and therefore is a mixture, not a pure chemical. Conversely, a synthetic, aromatic aldehyde, such as vanillin, is chemically pure although "artificial."

4. The solvent should be pure and not have an odor or flavor of its own that might linger in the oil. It should have a vapor pressure sufficiently different

from that of the oil so that separation by simple evaporation should be possible. It should be safe in terms of flammability and toxicity. The absence of traces of materials that would be toxic on ingestion is more important in flavors than in fragrances. Also, flavors should not combine or react with substances in foods to form toxic products.

18.3 • Nylon: A Thousand and One Uses

1. Nylon is composed of smaller units, called monomers.

2. Adipic (hexanedioic) acid plus hexamethylenediamine produces Nylon 66 plus water.

3. The molecules pack more closely together and become oriented along a single axis. Hydrogen bonds form between adjacent molecules.

4. Drawing increases the strength and elasticity of the nylon.

5. Nylon is wear-resistant, wrinkle-free, and impervious to biological action by bacteria, fungi, and insects. It also takes and holds dyes well.

6. The properties include strength, resistance to abrasion, and imperviousness to biological action by bacteria, fungi, and insects.

20 • Dynamite: Manufacturing an Explosive Combination

1. Rapid oxidation of a fuel is occurring, with the production of gases, such as carbon dioxide and water vapor, and the release of energy.

2. Different types of dynamite have different properties that make them suitable for particular applications.

3. Dynamite is manufactured in a continuous process. Glycerol is nitrated with acid under continuous cooling. The nitroglycerin moves through tubes and is mixed with oxidizers and other materials. Finally, the mixture is compressed into tubes.

4. The pressure decreases as the gas volume increases.